Control of engineering projects

ENGINEERING MANAGEMENT

Series Editor S. H. Wearne, BSc(Eng), PhD, CEng, Consultant, Director of Institution courses and in-company training

Editorial panel D. E. Neale, FICE; D. P. Maguire, BSc, FICE; D. J. Ricketts, BSc; B. A. O. Hewett, BSc(Eng), MSc, FICE; and J. V. Tagg, FICE

ENGINEERING MANAGEMENT

Control of engineering projects

Edited by
S. H. Wearne, BSc(Eng), PhD, CEng

Second edition

Thomas Telford Ltd, London

Published by Thomas Telford Ltd, Thomas Telford House,
1 Heron Quay, London E14 9XF

First published 1974 by Edward Arnold (Publishers) Ltd,
25 Hill Street, London W1X 8LL
Reprinted 1979
Second edition 1989

British Library Cataloguing in Publication Data
  Control of engineering projects
    1. Engineering. Projects. Management
    I. Wearne, Stephen
    620'.0068

ISBN: 0 7277 1387 6

Typeset in Great Britain by MHL Typesetting Limited, Coventry
Printed and bound in Great Britain by Billings & Sons, Limited,
Worcester

Preface

Once upon a time engineers were trained by apprenticeship, technological studies and time served in organizations that were making and maintaining goods or services. Most of these engineers were employed in design offices, in production or construction to apply their technical knowledge of how to create new products or structures.

In time the more energetic and responsible of them were put in charge of sections of work, as first-line supervisors of fellow engineers, craftsmen, technicians and trainees.

If they seemed able to cope, the next opportunity could see some of these engineers promoted into middle management, in charge of larger and more varied groups of people and the resources of a department or a project.

The engineer so promoted to this level found that his original technical experience was still vital to understanding the consequences of his decisions, but he now felt pressures different from those which he had been prepared for. The time available for considering any problem was short, yet the effects of his choice of a solution would be long-lasting. And the major restraints on solving problems were no longer technical — he was limited by costs, by what other people would accept, and by uncertainties in predicting either of these. He had to manage three different sets of relationships. With those above him he had to be concerned with the results of decisions. With those below him he had to be concerned that they should find agreeable solutions to problems. And to gain some flexibility to help reconcile these vertical demands, he had to try to achieve co-operation with fellow managers, most of whom were his competitors in ambition and differed in their professional values and in their views on the organization's future.

The organization survived. Its managers added to their specialist services of planning and cost control. They also perceived the problems of internal relationships. The engineering manager was sent on a course that gave him time to think and helped him appreciate his personal characteristics. He became aware of how he might develop his abilities to communicate and manage. But back in his job there remained the pressures of cost and time. These pressures grew. Resources became more expensive, and the projects became more complex yet fewer and each more critical to the organization's success.

It was lunch-hour conversations with fellow managers that led our hero to appreciate that the greatest problems originated in inadequate attention to analysing, discussing, selecting, planning and launching their new projects. They learnt this in a process of self-education that took time to influence attitudes and policy in their organization.

These lessons have been learnt more than once, in many industries. Experience is a great teacher, but can come too late or be incomplete or misleading. Experience needs to be collected and analysed, to demonstrate the reasons for successes and the causes of problems. Engineers and managers in industry have only limited time to try to do this. The present authors have had more opportunity. This book is one result. It is a collective effort. The authors have been responsible for decisions on projects in various industries. They have since thought about their experience in order to lecture to courses in project management. They have developed their conclusions into the chapters that make up this book. This has been written to help engineers to understand the interactions of cost and time on technical decisions and to assist them to review their experience and consider how to improve practice.

Chapter 1 is an introduction to ideas of planning, monitoring and all that is involved in controlling the engineering of new products, processes, structures, systems or any such project. In chapter 2 the selection and sanctioning of projects is considered, with particular reference to investments in manufacturing, and then in chapter 3 the planning of projects stage by stage and by various techniques. Next are three chapters dealing in turn with the financial control of public works, mechanical contracting and construction. The final chapter is a review of organizational means of achieving control. Some notes and references to further reading are given at the end of each chapter.

The chapters overlap a little, as do the real problems of predicting and controlling the cost, timing and value of projects in any industry. The authors refer to different examples. These are drawn from their own experience. They illustrate principles important in managing all sorts and sizes of project.

Acknowledgements

All of us are indebted to past and present colleagues, teachers, employers and others too numerous to name whose work has contributed to our ideas and experience, and to the organizations and individuals who have given support to the development of studies of project management. Our thanks are due to all of these. The results as they appear in this book are, of course, the sole responsibility of the authors.

We are grateful to H. R. Noon, formerly of Dunchurch Staff College, Rugby, for permission to reproduce Table 1.1, and to companies for the details given in Appendix 2.2. Appendix 3.1 is based on articles jointly by R. A. Milligan and D. F. Brooks which were published in *The Engineer* in April 1968.

Chapter 2 was originally written by David Elliott and has now been revised extensively by Mike Allen. Similarly, chapter 5 was originally written by Ken Kelsey and has been revised extensively by John Evans.

I personally am indebted to the fellowship provided by the British Steel Corporation that gave me the time to prepare sections of the first edition.

S. H. Wearne

Contents

1 Notions and principles

Definition of control
Control — 'to check or verify, and hence to regulate ... ' (*Shorter Oxford English Dictionary*); ' ... to make situations behave according to certain desired performance criteria' (S. Beer, *Decision and control*, Wiley, 1966).

The meaning of the word control seems obvious. These definitions will help in thinking about it and in studying what is involved. They could apply to any type of control, such as the relatively simple domestic example of a thermostat used to switch heating on or off when it senses that a resulting temperature has moved below or above a set value. More advanced mechanical and electrical systems are now increasingly used in industry to achieve the automatic control of many variables in continuous manufacturing. Textbooks on the natural and emergency control systems of animals describe related examples.[1]

Communications
In this book we are concerned with the complication that the evolution and creation of a new engineering product, process, structure or system depend on the work of a variety of people, and usually only temporarily employ the skills and resources of groups in several organizations with differing interests.[2] The success of each project therefore depends on communications between the organizations involved, to interest people, obtain data, establish objectives and anticipate problems.

A project consisting of altering or renewing an existing investment can involve similar complications. Industries are organized mainly in specialist units to gain the economic advantages of each unit developing an expertise likely to be employed on many pro-

1

jects. A disadvantage of grouping activities in this way is that people and their work are described in terms of what they do rather than why it is worth doing. The ultimate objectives of each project can be remote or uncertain to individuals who are working on only a specialist part of many projects. Opportunities to continue their recognized specialism can become their greater interest. They can become too busy to think.[3]

Objectives

From the start of a project its objectives should therefore be discussed, defined and stated, to guide the consequent decisions. The initial statement can be brief, and developed as the project proceeds.

It may sound obvious that objectives should be defined early on. It is obvious, yet it is not always done. Experience of various industries indicates that an initial investment of resources to analyse uncertainties and conflicts in objectives can have the greatest single influence on the eventual success of projects.

The need for control

Ideally, everybody should control their own commitments, to be responsible for deciding what they can and will do and be in direct contact with all the other people on whom they depend socially and materially. But rarely is this ideal of self control achieved in industry, even in carrying out small and relatively simple projects. This is because of the specialization and interdependence which have evolved as people and organizations have developed skills and knowledge to achieve results that are beyond the capacity of individuals or unorganized collaboration.

To make these systems humane is one of the problems of industrial societies.[4] Everyone is becoming more and more dependent on them. In these complex conditions the working objectives of a firm or any group of people can define only their part in greater systems of providing goods and services. Planning and monitoring are therefore required to relate their objectives to external changes. There is also the more obvious need to check for mistakes, lateness in obtaining agreements from people whose interests may be affected, unexpected problems in design, changes in the supplies of materials, or underestimation of the amount of completion work required. However well these may have been anticipated, checking

2

of the work as it proceeds is likely to be valuable in order to compare how it is going with what was expected and so be able to analyse differences while there is time to alter the form, quality, speed or cost of the remainder.

Systems of control

The choice of the system of control of a project should logically depend on the objectives of the investment. The system should also vary from one part of the work to another, to suit differences in the scale, variety, novelty and interdependence of activities, the speed and accuracy of control wanted, and the cost, goodwill and other resources used for this compared with the value of the control achieved. The next five chapters of this book review the methods and techniques that can be used, but before going on to these we should appreciate that all systems of control are similar in principle in consisting of the following series of decisions.

- Select the project and state its objectives.
- Plan the work and review the effects of changes.
- Establish a monitoring system to check and verify progress.
- Decide on any actions needed to alter the remaining work to complete the project.

Each of these is in turn the basis for the next.

The *selection, planning* and *monitoring* of projects are terms commonly used in discussing systems of control, and are now defined.

Selection

Selection is the initial step in studying what ideas for projects fit the organization's objectives and resources, evaluating the predicted cost and predicted value of proposals, and deciding in which (if any) to invest.[5]

As indicated in Fig. 1.1, the study of ideas should draw on three distinct sources of information: new ideas resulting from research, predictions of market demands, and the experience and records accumulated from previous projects. Cost and value have to be estimated by analysing differences from the results obtained from previous projects. Some planning and design may be required in order to derive sufficiently accurate estimates, particularly by considering novel problems and other risks that could affect much

3

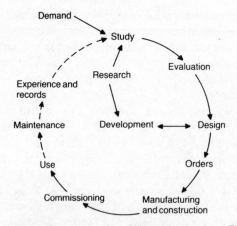

This shows the sequence of specialist activities employed. These specialisms can overlap. Most contribute indirectly to the final result. What matters is making best use of the investment of resources.

Fig. 1.1. Stages of work for an engineering project

of the work, but the essential task at this stage is to decide *whether* rather than *how* to proceed.[6]

These studies use some resources, but cost little in comparison with the value of making a sufficiently accurate decision to invest in the consequent project.

Planning

Planning is the process of making decisions in advance of the work on how to carry it out to determine *how best* to achieve the desired quality, cost and programme.

The planning can be simple, such as where the work to be done will consist of repeating familiar activities. Novel problems may have received attention earlier, but we will need to investigate potential difficulties to determine what other activities may be affected and decide how far to allow for alternative solutions. The purpose of planning is to predict the consequences of choices before choosing between them, particularly to anticipate problems of:

- *Critical activities* — the activities in the work for the project which in sequence will govern the time required to carry out the project, the duration for each of these activities usually being planned on the basis of the predicted value versus the predicted cost of various methods of work and concentrations of resources.

- *Interfaces* — the relationships between different groups' activities for a project, usually requiring detailed decisions on where, when and how they can fit together.

- *Safety* — the specification of precautions required for safety, as distinct from economy: particularly important in the erection and testing of urgent, novel or large projects.

- *Risks* — resources possibly needed for critical activities may have to be ordered early in the course of a project, although these may be affected by subsequent changes in the work required. If resources have to be specified despite these risks, planning is needed to indicate the probable consequences of changes and show how much freedom can be retained to follow alternatives. The more uncertain the initial information, the greater may be the value of advance planning and of reviewing the planning after each subsequent decision.

Starting from the predictions used when selecting a project, its design and planning should proceed together. Both consist of decisions on how to realize the project. They generate the instructions for the material work. Both provide the final basis for checking the predicted cost and value of proceeding with the major proportion of the investment. Both should draw on the detailed experience and records of previous projects, to utilize proven solutions to problems and avoid repeating mistakes such as unsafe erection methods or the poor employment of people.

Planning and design are processes in which the dimensions of information change — the input information that stated the objectives being transformed into the output detail of how to achieve them. The decisions made in planning are most often displayed in schedules and programmes showing the proposed sequence of work, timing of activities and use of specialists, machines and other resources, expressed numerically in terms such as expected progress per week. Fig. 1.2 shows the typical pattern of an activity or group of activities, the rate of working and the time for the work being the two dimensions of the results of the planning. Time is the independent variable; it is a unique resource, as we cannot store,

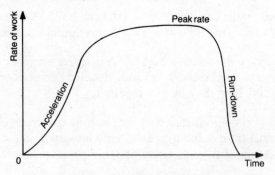

This shows the typical pattern of the rate of working for an activity or a group of activities. The initial acceleration of work can depend upon whether people are having to learn new skills and to work together. The rate of run-down at the end can depend upon how their work is affected by other activities or the prospects for their further empoyment.

Fig. 1.2. The pattern of work for a project

accelerate or reverse it. Dates and periods of time are therefore the primary dimensions of planning.

Planning is a means to the end of achieving a project. Its results should be used:

- to guide the ordering and use of resources,
- to provide the targets for monitoring the work.

Monitoring

Monitoring is the process during the work for a project of checking and verifying to compare actions and results with the predictions and intentions, in order to demonstrate what changes are needed to overcome problems and achieve objectives. This can involve repeating some or much of the earlier planning, to adapt to changes in objectives or unexpected problems.

To be used in time to alter the remaining work, monitoring has to be based upon measuring interim results during the progress of activities, and inferring from these measurements whether the final results will be satisfactory. This involves problems of technique encountered in making any type of measurement: the act of measuring disturbs the scene being measured and diverts some energy from the primary task of completing the project. Sampling

6

is therefore most common. The need for control action to change the work can then be decided by considering:

- *Error* — the difference between the measured rate of work and the rate that was required. Note that some range of difference between the two must be tolerated, to allow for inaccuracy in the measurements and to avoid acting on trivial amounts of error.

- *Rate of change* — the rate of change of the error: an indication that the error is increasing is important.

- *Accumulated error* — the integration of results up to the time of measurement compared with the total required, to indicate whether the remaining work must be re-planned and a new rate of work required.

Together these form a three-term basis for control, as used in mechanical, electrical and biological control systems.

The dimensions of planning and monitoring are not the same as the objectives of the project — they have the dimensions of the resources being used. Measurements should therefore be viewed in terms of their significance to the project. For instance, rather than ask when an activity will be complete we can better ask when the next activities can start.

Reviewing and learning

When reviewing a completed project in comparison with its original objectives in order to account for decisions and learn from the experience, we are too late to contribute to its control, but we can usefully include a review of the cost and value of the system of control used in each stage of the work.

Creating a control system is itself a project, requiring an investment of resources to achieve value. Novel or large control systems should therefore be formally controlled by a higher level of system designed to plan, monitor and correct them.

Balanced control

Expenditure on planning is of value only if it is useful in preparing the work to carry out a project. Expenditure on monitoring is of value only if it is useful in controlling the work as it proceeds. Both can be insufficient, or excessive. Logically, the expenditure

7

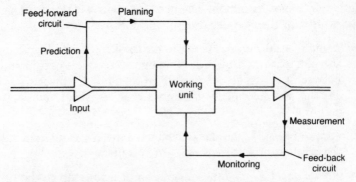

Planning is based on predictions of the work to come; monitoring on measuring the work when under way

Fig. 1.3.   Planning and monitoring for control

on the two should be matched to establish a balanced system of control.

Research studies of the control of projects have not yet produced numerical evidence to indicate how much can usefully be spent on planning and monitoring. However, we can be guided by conclusions from experience that certain symptoms indicate that a control system is faulty. These symptoms of control problems are listed in Table 1.1. This list is based upon the experience of engineers and managers attending project management courses. It includes the likely results of insufficient or excessive planning and control. Action to alter a system is probably needed if it shows most of the symptoms listed in one quadrant of this table.

Application of principles

In the next five chapters the authors discuss in turn the selection, planning and subsequent control of projects, illustrating these with some examples from their experience in industry. The application of the principles illustrated should logically vary from project to project and organization to organization. Examples and experience do not automatically apply to all other projects. Differences in technical content and in the uncertainty of decisions are obvious variables that should affect the choice of the control system. More broadly we should note that investments vary in the relative

8

Table 1.1.   Some opinions of indicators of over or under planning and control (Noon)*

	Underplanned	Overplanned
Undercontrolled	Plans and budgets not available Few routine reports Meetings only in crises Cash flow problems Staff complain of lack of direction, or erratic work loads Management dominated by personalities Many projects have priority High proportion of tenders lead to orders Poor relations with customers, particularly because of poor deliveries Poor, erratic profits No enthusiasm apparent	Plans out of date or 'the projects run the PERT' Few progress reports, all unrelated to plan Meetings triggered by crises Staff complain of lack of direction Management involved in details High proportion of tenders lead to orders Many projects have priority
Overcontrolled	Violent changes of direction Plans and budgets not available Extensive progressing activity not related to plans Frequent detailed meetings Cash flow problems Staff complain of frequent job changes Staff of low calibre 'Low level' personalities dominant No top management support for systems Customers exert pressure History of delivery crisis	Many forms and reports in evidence Frequent formal meetings Little cash flow difficulty Staff tend to be low calibre, leave work on time Top management enthusiasm for systems Programme and progress reporting at high level Poor tendering success rate Good relations with customers History of recent crisis and/ or management changes

*These lists are not exhaustive. They are indicators to be considered as a whole, so that action on a system should be taken if it shows most of the symptoms in any one quadrant.

importance of cost, time and value.[7] These categories of project are:

- *Commercial projects* — when a profit to the investor is expected at the completion of a reliable result. The predicted cost and timing of proceeding with the project should therefore be decided according to the predicted value of the result.

- *Minimum cost projects* — if little or no cash return to the spending organization is expected from completion of a project, the cost alone can remain as the influence on decisions. This tends to be the category of public works, where rarely are the resources provided to carry out projects at the socially most acceptable speed.

- *Emergency projects* — alternatively, the speed of action in carrying out a project can be overriding in its influence on decisions, and costs recorded only for accounting rather than for achieving economy in the use of resources.

Experience and examples from one category may therefore have to be modified for application to the others, depending on the differences in objectives and in the work to be done.

Notes
1. Any reader may find interesting the experimental games and resulting observations on control theory in: Hassenstein, B. *Information and control in the living organism*, Chapman & Hall, 1971.
2. See the companion book edited by Martin, A.S. and Grover, F.R. *Managing people*. Thomas Telford, London, 1988.
3. An extreme example of aimless effort portrayed by Messrs Barker and Corbett on BBC television showed two gardeners moving a hole from one end of a meadow to the other. To move the hole they dug a second nearby, filling the original one with the earth from the second, then dug a third hole and filled the second, and so on in the required direction. Any supervisor or quantity surveyor could have measured their progress accurately, and any planning expert could have optimized their earth-moving routine.
4. Handy, C. *Understanding organizations*, 3rd edn., Penguin, London, 1985.
5. The decision to invest resources in a project is also known as 'sanctioning' but note that this is an ambiguous word with the alternative meaning 'a penalty for disobedience'.

6. The selection process is usually based on what are called 'feasibility studies'. The result in some industries is called a performance specification: in others a project definition. It can be divided into stages, to invest a relatively small amount of resources in order to try to predict more accurately the cost and value of proceeding any further.

7. Cost, time and value can form the three parameters of objectives, the word 'value' including performance, quality, etc., as suggested by J.W. Hackney, *Control and management of capital projects*, Wiley, 1965.

2 Selection and sanctioning

This chapter is in two parts. The first part sets out principles for selecting between ideas for projects, to choose which are worth a share of the resources available. The importance of authoritative decisions is emphasized. The second part of the chapter describes the sanctioning of the use of resources to ensure that a chosen project is adequately evaluated and planned before committing most of the expenditure. Details of procedures needed to control manufacturing projects are discussed. The principles are applicable to all industries.

Selection

In most organizations in industry and the public services there are ideas for spending money to improve performance. These ideas exist at various stages of development, and in the earlier stages their demands on the organization's resources of money and manpower are relatively small. Sooner or later these ideas become sufficiently well formulated and they then require substantial resources for further development and implementation. Almost inevitably, several ideas reach this stage at roughly the same time. The aggregate demand on the organization's resources will nearly always be in excess of those available. Thus only a limited number of ideas proposed will be taken further. A selection process is therefore needed.

Each idea may have been nurtured by a manager who regards his idea as essential for the future well-being of the organization. Accordingly he may not eagerly admit that someone else's idea has prior claim on the resources of the organization. The rejection of many ideas put forward will inevitably lead to disappointment on the part of the originators of those ideas. To avoid this, it is better to carry out a preliminary selection as early as possible in a project's life. This reduces the abortive work involved and also prevents offending people's pride in their ideas.

The latter is probably the most important consideration, as the feeling of disappointment when an idea is rejected usually leads to a temporary reduction in the performance of the originator. The duration of this disappointment may be roughly proportional to the effort put into formulating the rejected proposal. This preliminary work should be limited to that adequate to allow an objective decision to be made on the merits of the proposal.

Decision levels of selection

By definition, projects are one-off activities of finite duration and of a cost that has been pre-specified before starting the project activity. In addition, projects are vehicles for change. An organization is always altered in some way at the end of any project. Projects therefore can conflict with routine in management. Furthermore, project ideas may originate in any part of an organization and usually have implications for other departments. For example, in manufacturing a minor change in the packaging of a product would have consequences in sales, distribution, production, supply, accounts and possibly others.

It is because of this cross-functional effect that a selection committee should be formed, made up of managers who are authorized both to sanction the appropriate expenditure of cash and, more importantly, to commit their particular functions to supply the manpower and other resources required for those projects selected. This almost automatically means that it will consist of senior managers within the organization. Any project of reasonable size interacts with the longer term policies of the organization and may be financially crucial to the survival of the organization. Thus all such projects need to be selected by the policy making body, e.g. the board of directors in a company or the council in local government. This tends to be the usual arrangement, major projects requiring their approval but minor projects being approved by a sub-committee or group of senior managers. The line of demarcation between major and minor projects is individual to an organization, and is not necessarily based purely on project cost.

New products, new processes or new markets of whatever size might all be defined as policy level decisions.

Objectives of selection

Because the selection of the most appropriate projects for any organization is not simple, it is best to have a deliberately formal procedure for selection. As well as requiring a specific level of information about each project put up for approval, this has the advantage of ensuring that all project work is only undertaken if authorized.

The selection decision is not simple to make. Before any project reaches the decision-making group for approval, it should have been analysed and agreed by the senior managers from where it originated. Thus the problem is not that of picking obvious winners, it is to make fine judgements between proposals of seemingly equal merit. No organization has infinite resources, and thus a viable project may have to be rejected sometimes because others at least equally good were competing with it when approval was sought. The problem of rendering the originator's recent work null and void — perhaps completely wasted — and certainly shelved for some time is that he or she is likely to be demotivated. His or her further ideas are still required, as a flow of new ideas is essential for the survival of any organization and this flow must not be cut off. Thus the selection procedure for projects has a difficult combination of objectives to achieve. These objectives are as follows:

- All projects selected must be viable with adequate returns.
- All non-viable projects must be rejected.
- Good projects should not be rejected without good reason.
- The flow of project proposals must not be discouraged.

The first two objectives are fairly easy to achieve by installing adequate procedures. The latter two are far more involved with management judgements in particular circumstances. But if they are not achieved, long term survival of the organization is threatened.

With these objectives in mind, the next step is to consider the criteria that will form the basis of the selection decision and thus also form the basis of sanctioning.

Criteria for selection of projects

It is unfortunate that the criteria for selecting projects are not absolute and immutable. Although there is the overriding requirement for a project to be profitable, or advantageous in some other way, considerations are also involved that are likely to vary with time and with the state of development of the organization.

Policy and strategy

Any proposals should relate to the organization's policy and strategy for survival and growth. If in a manufacturing company, there is a long term plan for diversification, then projects aimed at producing more of the existing products, albeit more efficiently, tend to be regarded with less favour than a project aimed at introducing a new product for a different market. Conversely, if the product line is being rationalized then proposals for new products or for producing fringe products more efficiently are unlikely to gain approval. Good control is needed to avoid resources being diverted, against policy, into this 'continuation' type of project.

The political and economic situation

This is important on the strategic time-scale and will obviously affect the availability of funds for projects and the criteria for selecting and controlling them. In times of economic growth and when substantial investment incentives are available, the amount of investment in projects is likely to be much higher than average. During economic recessions many projects will be postponed or cancelled.

Project competition

Competition for resources varies, not only between new projects for sanctioning but also between projects in hand that utilize the same resources. Most projects cannot be stopped once started without becoming grossly uneconomical. So the projects selected as the best at the time are not necessarily the best projects as they proceed. Better projects presented later may be rejected because the environment has changed and resources already committed are not available. Thus to a manager seeking approval of a particular project the phasing relative to other projects is often vital. For example, it could be that some resources are under-utilized and it is better to relax the selection criteria rather than disperse a design team of proven experience. Thus a marginally unacceptable project might be approved at that time. Frequent sanctioning of marginally unacceptable projects must be avoided, as poor returns from many projects is likely to lead to the failure of a business.

15

Project capacity and demand

The size of a project is significant. Is the organization able to deal with a very big project? Is it better to have several small projects than one big one? To a large extent the answers depend on the management available within the organization. The financial risk for an organization is much greater if it has one major project rather than a portfolio of smaller ones, but in the latter case all or most of the projects must help fulfil the organization's strategy.

Organizational health

A consideration can sometimes be the organization's health. If the organization is in financial difficulties, quick short-term action may be needed. The organization may not survive without the short-term action, but emphasis on only short-term performance may cause neglect of long-term needs such as research and development. Survival and growth will eventually suffer.

Competitors

The activities of competitors and potential competitors are obviously relevant to investment decisions. Many projects have been quickly put together in reply to competitive activity, to the detriment of more worthwhile ones. Some projects are or should be stopped if a competitor has acted much faster.

Profitability

Even with all the considerations already mentioned, the major one in a commercial environment is the resultant profitability.[1]

The required profitability, however calculated, may vary from time to time in an organization for any of the reasons discussed above. It depends upon taxation rates, grants and capital allowances which may be changed by governments at short notice. Furthermore, a project's profitability may well depend upon the risk involved. Usually, the high-risk projects will need high profitability to be acceptable and, conversely, low risk means that a lesser profitability is acceptable.

Risk

In all project activity, the profitability that is quoted at the early stages of the project life is only a forecast and like all forecasts is subject to error.

This uncertainty in the outcome arises from unforeseen changes in the large number of factors that can affect a project. It is worthwhile to consider these factors in detail as the implications need to be understood in order to quantify the risk. This quantification of the risk is the underlying rationale of any sanctioning procedure. The problem arises because forecasts can change during the time taken to carry out a project and many things can happen that were not foreseen at the time of seeking sanction. The broad problem areas are discussed below.

Initial costs of projects. These often escalate alarmingly for many reasons apart from bad estimating.[2] Raw material prices may increase, labour rates may increase, design snags may be found, etc.

On-going running costs. At the time of sanction, assumptions are made about staff costs, raw material costs and maintenance costs involved in carrying on whatever system is to be produced by the project. This applies to any project, whether its outcome is a new administration system, a new factory, a new distribution system, etc.[3] The initial assumptions may well prove to be wrong and usually underestimated rather than over-estimated.

Market estimates. Forecasting the future sales of existing products in existing markets is difficult enough; forecasting the sale of new products in new markets can only be a reasoned 'guestimate'.

Equally difficult is the forecasting of competitive activity. Allowance must always be made in commercial markets for some degree of retaliation on the part of a competitor. Worse still, a competitor can reach the market with a new product which will seriously affect the market forecasts.

Degree of innovation. To a large extent, this is related to the previous factors and is the cause of uncertainty in those areas. New technology or new market sectors pose different problems to a company, even if other companies are already using the technology or are operating in the market. The ability of the organization to react to these new problems is always in doubt until they actually occur.

Ancillary costs. When a project is in the process of being implemented there is usually some disruption in the normal activities of the organization. At the end of the implementation period, a new situation exists and the organization takes time to settle down to this new situation. The time to reach a new normality depends, in the first instance, upon the scale of the disruption. However, the cost of this disruption is often underestimated, sometimes consciously assumed to be negligible and sometimes completely ignored.

To illustrate this point, consider the installation of plant to produce a new product complementary to the existing range. If the new product is an extension to the range, and is non-competitive with the existing products, it is easy to assume that there will be no change in sales of the old products. But the sales force are bound to put their energy and expertise into selling the new product rather than on maintaining the sales level of the old ones. This may well lead to a decline in sales of the old products because most sales levels need constant effort to maintain them. At best there is likely to be a temporary loss of sales, but this temporary loss might be easily turned by a competitor into a permanent loss. The cost of this loss should have been considered as part of the project cost for the new product.

Other costs could be relatively minor ones such as new stationery, changes in the accounting systems, etc. Often the aggregate of these individually small costs is surprisingly large and should have been included when assessing the project. The unforeseen nature of some of these costs contributes to the risk involved in any project.

Sensitivity analysis

Capital projects may be evaluated using a number of different financial techniques (see Appendix 2.1 for the main ones). Regardless of the technique used the financial evaluation is represented by a *single* figure, e.g. internal rate of return = 27·4%.

It is too easy for people to believe that since the 'answer' is calculated precisely that it must be correct. The actual outcome of a project, however, is almost certain to be different from that forecast.

Sensitivity analysis is concerned with *how much* the financial return is affected by deviations from forecast. For instance, if the selling price of a project's output falls by 10%, by how much will the internal rate of return fall? It is often useful to determine the effect on a project's financial return of changes in the following:

- sales price
- sales (and output) volume

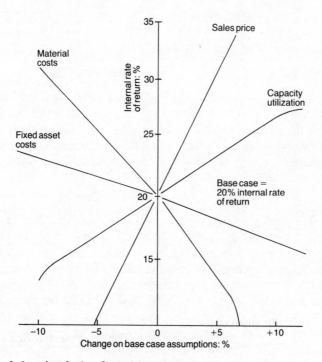

Fig. 2.1. Analysis of sensitivity

- material costs
- date when project comes on stream
- fixed asset costs
- stock levels
- life of project.

Fig. 2.1 illustrates how to use sensitivity analysis to identify which factors affect a project's financial outcome most. In this instance the financial outcome is most sensitive to changes in sales price.

Sensitivity analysis considers changes to these (input) factors *one at a time*. Although it is relatively easy to assess the effect of an error in forecasting one factor alone, errors are likely to be present in all factors, in both magnitude and direction. The combined effect of these errors can be difficult to assess unless a formal analysis is carried out in order to quantify the sensitivity to errors.

19

Table 2.1. The sensitivity of the rate of return to errors in forecasting is best appreciated by calculating the returns in a number of possible situations and tabulating the results

Sales volume V	Capital cost C		
	10% below	Expected	10% above
10% below	R_{11}	R_{21}	R_{31}
Expected	R_{12}	$\boxed{R_{22}}$	R_{32}
10% above	R_{13}	R_{23}	R_{33}

In its simplest form, this analysis could take the form of constructing a matrix of profitability as shown in Table 2.1. In this example errors in forecast of only two major components are considered. Once again the example is taken of a project to install a production plant within a manufacturing company. The two main components that are considered are capital cost and sales volume. A 3 × 3 matrix is constructed showing the financial outcomes predicted for three levels of the two factors. The levels chosen for each factor could conveniently be the expected level, 10% above the expected level and 10% below the expected level.

This type of matrix can be constructed with several more levels for each factor, e.g. 5%, 10%, 15%, 20%, 25%, etc. It is rather more difficult to handle more than two factors, although a computer can be used. It could well be that a complete model should be developed to enable this more sophisticated analysis to be performed. Whether this is worthwhile depends upon the projects concerned.

Other methods of dealing with risk assessment

Sensitivity analysis gives information on how much the financial return is affected by specified changes to input factors (sales price, output volume, etc.) It does not predict *how likely* these changes are to occur. Often output volumes and prices differ widely from the original forecast. Labour costs and (sometimes) fixed asset costs may be much more predictable.

One of the ways to deal with uncertainty in the forecast estimates of sales volume etc., is to ask the company's experts (in this case

Table 2.2. Forecast probabilities for achieving various sales volumes

Probability	Sales volume
0·1	5600 000
0·3	5200 000
0·4	4800 000
0·2	4000 000

the sales/marketing department) to forecast the probabilities of possible outcomes (see Table 2.2).

Although this method may be time-consuming, relies on subjective estimates, and might mislead the unwary into believing these estimated probabilities are actual probabilities, it does utilise the best knowledge within the organization to assess the likelihood of various outcomes and hence their effect on the financial return.

The probabilistic analysis approach outlined here can be taken one stage further by using the forecast probability information in a computerised simulation. In this approach random selections are made from the probability distributions of sales price, sales volume,

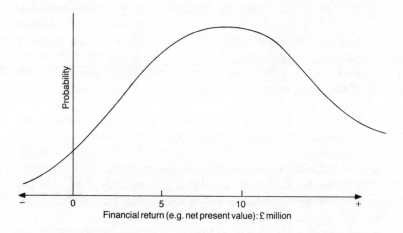

Fig. 2.2. Output from computerized simulation of a project's probability against net present value

fixed asset cost, material costs etc., and the financial return is calculated. The computer is able to repeat this calculation quickly, perhaps two hundred times, and plot a graph showing the probability of varying financial returns, such as shown in Fig. 2.2. Although this type of simulation has been used for a number of years it has not become widely adopted.

Other less exotic methods of coping with risk are:

- to establish a minimum payback period
- to limit the project life, for evaluation purposes
- to use a higher discount rate for 'risky' projects.[4]

Obtaining reliable information

All engineering projects involve a measure of risk, but the level of risk can be lowered by obtaining the best available information on which to evaluate the project. This means seeking help from those most knowledgeable about the various aspects of the project.

- Sales and marketing personnel are the most likely source of best estimates of sales volumes and prices and credit terms to be offered, together with promotion and selling costs. They are also best placed to identify external sources of information to supplement their own estimates.
- Buyers can provide the most expert advice on the availability, price (and discounts), and quality of bought in materials and components. In addition to their known sources they are best able to seek out other supply sources. In fact some organizations employ staff whose sole job is to seek out new (and better) sources of supply. This is hardly surprising because the cost of purchases in many engineering companies accounts for about half of total costs.
- Production and work study personnel can provide estimates of labour availability, production times, and supervision requirements.
- Finance and accounting staff can provide details of wage rates, salaries, building occupancy and utilities costs. They will also identify the acceptable financial targets for satisfactory projects (e.g. minimum internal rate of return).
- Engineering staff, between them, should then be able to identify capital equipment availability and costs, tooling costs, maintenance costs, effects on stock levels, project life and any

subsequent removal costs of capital equipment (e.g. North Sea oil platforms).

Within the organization full use of the available expertise needs to be utilised in planning and evaluating engineering projects, as well as in their subsequent control. The individual responsible for preparing the project details for evaluation must have the necessary social skills to obtain the help and support of others. It is in the interests of all departments that every attempt is made to sort out the good potential projects from the rest. The future of the company and its employees depend on it.

The sanctioning of projects

The preceding sections of this chapter illustrated the problem of selecting viable projects by consideration of the criteria used to make the selection. It was pointed out that because of the uncertainties inherent in a project, a combination of adverse circumstances could arise that would result in a quite unacceptable financial return. The remainder of this chapter discusses the use of a formal procedure for project sanction as a means of minimizing the risk of selecting projects that might ultimately fail to produce the return required by the organization.

It cannot be emphasized too strongly that no procedure is able to provide a one hundred per cent guarantee against unrewarding projects. No procedures can turn bad estimates into good ones. The procedure is only as good as the people within the organization and shoddy work remains shoddy work however much pseudo-respectability it is given by being dressed up in accordance with a formal procedure.

The imposition of a formal procedure has two major advantages: firstly, the procedure at its most basic ensures that all projects have their expected financial return properly calculated and also that it conforms with the organization's standards; secondly, it ensures that there is a common agreed level of information provided for all projects when presented for selection. The strict discipline it imposes also reduces the temptation for both decision makers and proposers alike to take short cuts. Hasty decisions based on inadequate information may well lead to disaster.

The other major point about a sanction procedure is that it deals with only one project at a time. The selection decision between competing projects is a matter of management judgement — a judgement based on the facts that are presented about each project in accordance with the sanctioning procedure. No procedure can replace this exercise of management skill, but at least a formal procedure for sanctioning projects should prevent the occurrence of major errors in selection.

A project sanctioning procedure

At its simplest, a sanctioning procedure is a means by which the organization ensures that money and other resources are not wasted on projects that fail to meet its own investment criteria. If this were all that was required it would merely be a financial exercise: however, it is also necessary to ensure that the projects undertaken fit in with the longer term plans for the organization, to minimize risk of loss, to minimize abortive work, etc.

A sanctioning procedure works by requiring a pre-specified set of facts about the project to be presented to a decision-making body. Typically, the facts required are as follows:

- purpose and description of project
- justification of estimated sales volume and price (total market and percentage share)
- justification of estimated operating costs and description of production methods and plant, capacity utilization
- capital expenditure (estimated/quotation/contingency allowance)
- other financial factors (grants/tax allowances/working capital)
- use of existing plant
- financial returns (IRR, NPV, payback, etc.)
- cash flow (maximum cash exposure)
- sensitivity analysis (e.g. effect on IRR of ±10% change in volume of sales, sales price, operating costs, capital expenditure)
- major risks involved
- labour, management, administration resources needed
- design of plant
- non-financial benefits of the project
- effect of project on total company position
- conclusions and recommendations

The list will vary with the objectives of an organization and its types of project, but the facts required will be essentially the same.

The accuracy with which any of the items can be stated depends on the stage of development of the project. Before undertaking any large expenditure, estimates must be sufficiently accurate to give a high probability that an adequate financial return will be achieved.

For small projects or projects that are repeats of previous ones, the decision could be made quickly. For large-scale projects, particularly those dependent on innovation, it is almost impossible to produce all the cost estimates, sales forecasts, etc., with sufficient accuracy for a final implementation decision unless a fairly large amount of development work is first carried out on the project. For major engineering projects this 'pre-sanction' design work could easily add up to a few man-years of design effort. In terms of elapsed time it could spread over several months or even years. This type of work may be complex, requiring the attention of senior managers and skilled staff. Both are in short supply in any organization.

More than saving money, it is important to avoid the waste of managerial time that would be involved if a lot of work was done on a project that was later rejected. Money is relatively easy to obtain but it is much more difficult to augment managerial skill, particularly with people who not only have the skill but also know the particular organization. Thus the large-scale or innovatory project requires a much earlier decision to be made — long before it is possible to produce sanction estimates of high accuracy — in order to minimize abortive work. This first decision as to whether or not to proceed with a project must be taken very early in the project life cycle, as part of the initial study phase. The facts about the project that have to be presented to the decision makers are the same as those in the final decision stage, but of course the accuracy of such things as cost and sales estimates is only indicative, e.g. with a one in five chance of not being wrong by more than $\pm 33\%$.

At this stage in the project life the decision is dependent on policy: does the project fit in with other projects being undertaken, does it fit into the longer term plans for the organization, would it mean large scale changes within the organization, etc., rather than with the forecast profitability, which is known to be only a guestimate? Obviously, it must be clear that the project has a good chance of being proved viable but it must be realized that this is based

25

necessarily on predictions that are subject to wide margins of error.

So far the procedure has been shown to have two decision points, one at the very beginning of the project and the other at the final commitment stage. On complex, innovatory projects the amount of development work needed to refine the initial estimates to be sufficiently accurate is often rather large. In these cases it is worthwhile having intermediate decisions taken at suitable stage points within the development work. This then gives the organization the opportunity to cut its losses on the project should it be seen to be failing to live up to its early promise. The data presented at the review stages are similar to those at the initial decision, but updated and more accurate.

Thus the project sanctioning procedure consists of at least two points at which a specified range of data concerning the project is presented for approval. At either point the decision can be made to proceed with the project or not. Intermediate decision points may be specified as required. The level of management empowered to make decisions to invest must be formally specified, together with the timing of the decision points and the range of data required at each. The working of such a procedure is now illustrated.

Sanctioning procedure in manufacturing industry

In the manufacturing industries the ideas which lead to project proposals may arise anywhere in the company. In a high technology company the research department may be the source of a new project that is taken on through development and engineering departments. In a consumer goods industry the technology is usually well defined and often the marketing department originate projects to take advantage of a market opportunity they have identified or any department may suggest substantial modification of an existing product to improve its competitiveness or extend its market.

Wherever an idea originates, the typical stages through which the idea develops are as follows:

- 1. Statement of the idea
- 2. Market research to help define the demand
- 3. Approximate product definition
- 4. Laboratory-scale production

- 5. Pilot-scale production
- 6. Precise product definition
- 7. Design of full-scale production plant
- 8. Construction of full-scale production plant
- 9. Full-scale production.

In a large-scale process industry all these stages are needed, but in less technically complex industries either or both of stages 4 or 5 could be omitted. The project sanctioning procedure now has to be fitted to these stages.

At stage 1 very little effort has been put into the basic idea. After all, the objective of research or marketing is the generation of ideas, particularly for new products. Equally, the marketing budget often includes within it an allowance for market studies aimed at either identifying new opportunities or evaluating the potential of ideas originated by other departments; so the initial costs up to and including stage 2 of the project are covered as part of the on-going, routine departmental costs. If a sanctioning procedure was started on a project-by-project basis this early it could discourage ideas. Few people in industry like exposing ideas until they have had some chance to develop them and formulate them reasonably well. Also many cases could be cited when the true significance of a research idea has only become apparent at a late stage in the research process, and this is so for marketing ideas as well.

Once an idea has been developed to stage 3, a product definition is produced for approval, as further development would depend on using the resources of other departments for whom the work involved will not necessarily be part of their routine operation.

Initial screening of projects

Stage 3 in the above list was called the approximate product definition. This is part of the *Study* stage of a proposal as illustrated in Fig. 1.1. When the product has been defined, albeit approximately, there exists the possibility of evaluating its potential. The information required at this stage would vary from industry to industry and product to product, but in most manufacturing industries the following statements and predictions would be expected:

- Marketing
- o market sector

27

o market size and expected growth
o own share of market
o competitive activity within market sector
o volume of sales and sales price, e.g. 100,000 tonnes per year at £50 per tonne.

- Sales and distribution
o methods of selling
o packaging
o method of launching
o effect on existing products
o distribution methods
o launch costs.

- Design
o estimated capital costs
o estimated operating costs
o timing
o degree of innovation.

- Production
o production rate, e.g. 100,000 tonnes per year
o wastage
o staffing plan, e.g. 10% extra direct labour
o direct costs
o indirect costs.

- Finance
o required gross margin, e.g. £10 per tonne
o capital allowances and taxation
o cash flows
o internal rate of return.

The appropriate definition of the product allows the engineers to work up an initial estimate of the capital cost. This, together with the other cost estimates, allows the accountants to evaluate the project considering the effects of taxation, inflation, grants, etc.

At this stage all the information may be rather uncertain, as considerable further work is required to be more accurate. But the data are sufficient for a first screening decision. This decision should be taken formally and recorded. The project then has a life of its own. It has been given a 'birth certificate'. Also, more significantly, it is given some order of priority so that everyone who needs to, knows how the project ranks in its demands on the company's resources.

Unfortunately the communication of decisions on priorities is often neglected. Obviously, if an idea is rejected, only the originators need to be told, together with some explanation for its rejection. However, when the decision is made to go ahead with the project, clear notification of that fact should be given to all who will be involved.

Everyone needs to be quite clear what is sanctioned at this initial screening stage — it is *not* the project itself. What is being implied by an affirmative decision is that work may be undertaken so that the uncertainty in project outcome may be reduced to an acceptable level. The amount of work required for this has been estimated and thus a limit set on development expenditure relating to the project. Equally, what is to be achieved by this expenditure is clearly specified. For example, if a project proposal asks for £100 000 to evaluate a pilot scale system prior to the preparation of full scale, final commitment estimates, then a failure to complete the evaluation in spending the £100 000 is reported and sanction sought for further expenditure to complete the evaluation and *not* for the whole project. Many projects turn out to be failures because too little is spent on the early exploratory work. Favourable indications from incomplete evaluations are not sufficient. If it was not fully carried out then either the requirement for the evaluation was wrongly stated or else risks are being taken that were originally not going to be taken.

These early development expenditures need to be controlled, for it is surprisingly easy to affect the viability of the full scale project, particularly as they are expended early in the life cycle of the project and the income to pay for them will not be received for some time, and all such costs have to be paid for whether the potential projects go ahead or not.

Intermediate review decisions

The possible need for more than the initial screening prior to the final commitment has been discussed. This need arises in large-scale projects with a reasonable innovation content which will necessitate major exploratory work being undertaken before

29

technical and commercial estimates can be produced to a sufficient accuracy for the final decision.

If the industry is based on simple, well-understood technology
or, alternatively, if the project consists of a comparatively minor
adaptation of an existing product, albeit technologically complex
to produce, then this intermediate decision stage is often unnecessary because the range of uncertainties is limited and the possible
effects on the profitability of the project are correspondingly
small.

Typically, the first intermediate review decision takes place prior
to embarking on pilot scale production. Further reviews, if required, are taken during this stage. By the time the project has
reached precise product definition most of the development, though
not all design, has been completed.

The information presented concerning the project at the intermediate decision stages is essentially the same as that presented
for the initial decision, but the estimates involved should be much
more accurate. Failure to increase the accuracy of these estimates
will mean the expenditure on development has been wasted. Similar
remarks apply to the relative accuracy of the information at subsequent intermediate decision points. If the accuracy is not increasing,
money is being wasted.

As with the initial screening, an affirmative intermediate decision does not sanction the project itself; merely the necessary money
for further development to take place. This staged development
continues for as many stages as are necessary before final sanction. The expenditure on development has to be controlled in the
same way as the ultimate project expenditure is controlled.

The type of work in these development stages could take many
forms, obviously depending on the type of project. It is not only
limited to pilot scale production. During this stage, variations on
the proposed new product could be evaluated using a reasonably
large-scale sample. Various packaging styles could be evaluated,
sizes, shapes, sales units, etc. The possible variations are too
numerous to attempt to list them, but all this evaluation work is
aimed at arriving at the best product and hence the most economical
project, reducing the uncertainties in predicting the outcome of
the final project. The review stages are not only concerned with
technical matters but include many 'commercial' considerations
as well.

Final commitment

Eventually, after the initial screening decision and any intermediate review stages, final approval needs to be given to the full scale investment. At this stage resources are committed, together with a large amount of management time. The information on which this final decision is based should be comprehensive, reasonably accurate and made prior to the design of the full-scale plant. Probable headings for a new product introduction are as follows:

- General
  - product/project reference number and description
  - general outline highlighting any novel features.

- Marketing
  - market analysis
  - nature of market
  - expected growth of market
  - expected growth of market share
  - possible competitive reaction
  - outline of launch plan.

- Sales
  - sales quantities by geographical area, customer etc.
  - expected growth during first year
  - change in sales of existing products resulting from the introduction of this new product
  - outline of launch plan.

- Production
  - end product specification
  - intermediates specifications
  - packaging specification
  - raw materials specifications
  - distribution plan
  - production plan
  - material supply plan
  - inventory investment
  - manpower and training requirements
  - management development.

- Engineering
o plant description
o project plan.

- Prices and costs
o selling price of product
o raw material prices
o prices of intermediates
o labour costs
o discounts
o launch costs
o project capital costs
o associated revenue costs.

- Finance
o financial return (IRR, NPV, payback, etc.)
o sensitivity analysis
o cash flow statement
o funding plan.

This list represents a considerable amount of detail for the new product. The list may be varied slightly from one situation to another but the outline still holds good. If the decision is made on the basis of these facts it will be an informed decision secure in the knowledge that the project proposed has been constructed with adequate planning and forethought. No procedure will completely eliminate the unforeseen problems that arise afterwards and inflate costs or prove sales estimates too high when the project is finally implemented, but the thought required in the preparation of the data will make the outcome as certain as it can be in an uncertain world.

This multiple-staged sanctioning procedure for new product introduction is equally applicable to other types of project in other types of organization. To start a new data processing system is just as much a project as is a new manufacturing plant. No major capital works will be involved and the pay-off is probably smaller in absolute terms. However, there are design costs and implementation costs which need to be evaluated and controlled. Another type of non-engineering project to which the procedure should apply is the reorganization of a distribution system; in effect any major change in the operating routine of an organization probably should be treated as a project and sanctioned accordingly. It is too often the case that changes which cause organizational and other disruptions costing many thousands of pounds are decided on whim or specious criteria without the adequate thought and planning that a sanctioning procedure would make necessary. Change requires planning and control; part of the control depends on a sanctioning procedure that ensures both the viability of the proposed change and its compatibility with other changes proposed or already affecting the organization.

The sanctioning procedure and project control

The sanctioning documents define the project and thus provide the objectives of the project control system. During the early life of a project when the outcome is uncertain, the control applies to the development work. Once the final commitment is made then the control is on the implementation of the project, the specifications and project plan, etc., forming the basis of the control. The sanction stages are thus as key nodes within a project planning network. All activities come into a decision node and since further activities are conditional on approval, then they must logically follow from that decision node. Thus, pictorially, a notational control network would be as shown in Fig. 2.3.

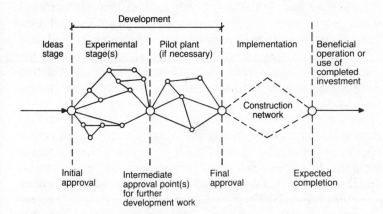

Fig. 2.3. Work at all stages of development of a project should be planned and controlled. Planning networks will converge at points where approval for further work is required

Sanctioning documents

An example of a set of forms used in sanctioning projects is shown in Appendix 2.2. A wealth of information is presented by this procedure to the decision makers at a fairly early stage in the life of the project. With good control procedures as the project proceeds, most of the problems disappear.

Summary

Although the criteria for selection of projects are qualitatively the same for all projects, the actual quantitative criteria vary from organization to organization, from project type to project type, and even with time within the one organization for similar projects.

A multiple-staged sanctioning procedure is recommended. The aims of this are to ensure that projects fit into the longer term objectives of the organization and that sufficient work is carried out to reduce the uncertainties to acceptable levels. Within the procedure, expenditure is sanctioned in one or more stages to produce increasingly more reliable statements on viability. Thus the decision-making authority has the opportunity of reviewing the proposal as it progresses through defined stages before taking a final commitment decision.

In addition to the specific project-oriented objectives, the sanction procedure also aims to reduce the amount of work undertaken for projects that may turn out to be uneconomic. This has the double advantage of saving the costs of abortive work and of avoiding unnecessary disillusionment of project originators.

The various stages of sanctioning are key points in a project control system. The combination of effective sanctioning and effective project control should avoid many of the problems associated with large scale projects. However, in the end, it is the quality of the management judgement that is the vital factor. Procedures are an adjunct to good management, not a substitute for it.

Notes

1. The financial criterion in public works equivalent to profitability is considered further in chapter 4.
2. The need to account for the escalation of prices is considered in later chapters, particularly chapter 5.
3. *Review of project performance audits*, World Bank, 1984.
4. For a summary of the discounted cash flow theory and other methods of assessing projects see Appendix 2.1.

Basic reading

Allen, D.H. *A guide to the economic evaluation of projects*, 2nd edn. Institution of Chemical Engineers, London, 1980.

De la Mare, R.F. *Manufacturing systems economics*. Holt, Rinehart and Winston, London, 1982.

Hayes, R.W. *et al*. *Risk management in engineering construction*. Thomas Telford, 1986.

Merrett, A.J. and Sykes, A. *The finance and analysis of capital projects*, 2nd edn. Longman, London, 1973.

Mott, G. *Investment appraisal for managers*. Pan Books, London, 1983.

Pike, R.H. *Capital budgeting in the 1980s*. Chartered Institute of Management Accountants, London, 1982.

Pilcher, R. *Appraisal and control of project costs*. McGraw-Hill, London, 1973.

Appendix 2.1. Capital investment appraisal methods for evaluation of proposed projects

Some capital projects *must* be undertaken in order to meet legal requirements, or in order just to continue in business. The alternative is to suffer the legal consequences or closure. Projects which are not compulsory or obligatory should be undertaken only if thought to be advantageous to the organization.

Although many proposed projects have identifiable positive financial results, some (or all) of the benefits arising from a capital investment might be non-financial. These latter benefits may be evaluated with the aid of cost-benefit analysis, comparing the measurable cost with the subjective benefits. Strategic considerations may lead top management to undertake some projects that are not themselves expected to be profitable, in order to enhance the long-term future prospects of the organization as a whole.

Although capital investment decisions should take into account both financial and non-financial information, this appendix is concerned only with the financial implications of potential projects. Financial evaluation is appropriate where the organization is free to decide whether or not to go ahead with a project, or where it can choose between several alternatives which will satisfy an obligatory requirement.

In deciding whether a proposed project is financially worthwhile, the value of the expected benefits must be predicted and compared with the estimated cost. The financial decision is dependent on these estimates, but the following appraisal methods should be more reliable than personal preference or guesswork.

35

Capital investment appraisal methods

Four popular investment appraisal methods are discussed, as follows:

- payback
- return on capital employed
- discounted cash flow: net present value
- discounted cash flow: internal rate of return

In practice, many companies use two or more of these appraisal methods in making investment decisions.

Payback

The payback period is the time taken for the positive cash benefits from a project to equal the cash invested in that project. For example, if £100 000 is invested in capital equipment resulting in cash savings of £40 000 per year, then the payback period will be $2\frac{1}{2}$ years. With some projects the positive cash benefits may be small to begin with but increase with time. The payback method is just as valid for these projects.

The payback method is simple and therefore easily understood. Its major drawback, however, is that it ignores the amount and duration of cashflows *after* the payback period.

Return on capital employed

Also known as return on investment (or ROI), return on capital employed measures the percentage profit (after depreciation) of a project as against its capital cost. For example, consider a capital investment of £10 000 yielding savings of £3000 per year for the next five years. Assuming the capital equipment has no residual value and that the £10 000 capital cost is depreciated by £2000 per year over the five years then the return on capital employed is 10% per year as follows:

average profit per year = £3000 (savings) − £2000 (depreciation)
= £1000
capital employed = £10 000
return on capital employed = £1000/£10 000 = 10% per year

Acceptable percentage rates of return need to be established for different types of investments with different expected project lives. Although the total returns from a project are taken into account the averaging process ignores the *timing* of profits. It is clearly better for profits to be made in the early years of a project rather than the latter years, given a specific average profit level.

Discounted cash flow — net present value

The net present value (NPV) method is one of the two main discounted cash flow (DCF) methods. DCF methods are concerned with discounting the *incremental cash flows* of an organization, in relation to a specific project. Past cash flows are irrelevant as they have already happened regardless of the decision. Depreciation, which is an accounting charge not involving cash flows, is also ignored. The cash flow associated with new capital is *incremental* and must therefore be included in the calculations. The calculations are best done in money terms (not real terms) and take account of taxation.

Discounting is the reverse of compounding. Compound interest calculations involve the formula:

$$S = P(1+r)^n$$

where S is the sum arising in the future year n, P is the sum at present (the principal), r is the interest rate per year expressed as a decimal and n is the number of years compounding, e.g. at 10% per year, £100 compounds to £121 in two years, as follows:

$$S = £100 \ (1+0 \cdot 1)^2 = £121$$

In discounting, the *present value* of future receipts or payments is the objective. The compounding formula is rearranged to give:

$$P = \frac{S}{(1+r)^n}$$

For example, the *present value* of £121 receivable in two years' time if interest is 10% per year is as follows:

$$P = \frac{£121}{(1+0 \cdot 1)^2} = £100$$

This means that £121 receivable in two years' time is *equivalent* to £100 today if interest is applied at 10% per year. Thus for any capital project the incremental cash flows for future years can be expressed in *net* present value terms.

Net present value is the arithmetic sum of the positive present values minus the negative present values as clarified below:

- Positive present values result from:
  o more cash in (e.g. increased net revenues)
  o less cash out (e.g. cost savings).

- Negative present values result from:
  o less cash in (e.g. lost sales from other products)
  o more cash out (e.g. payments for capital equipment).

Table 2.3

Year	Cash flow £	Discount factor	Present value
0	−9000	1·0	−£9000
1	+4000	0·9091	+£3636
2	+4000	0·8264	+£3306
3	+4000	0·7513	+£3005
Net present value			+£947

If the *net present value* is positive then the project is deemed financially viable.

In compounding the interest rate is referred to, but in discounting the term discount rate is used. The discount rate is usually calculated by the finance department and takes account of the organization's cost of capital which relates to the mix and cost of long-term loans and the shareholders' investment. The discount rate, however, may be varied to take into account different levels of risk, i.e. an expansion project may be discounted at a higher discount rate than a cost savings project, to compensate for its higher level of risk. Discount tables giving the discount factors at particular discount rates r and particular years n into the future help simplify the calculations of present values.

Example. A project involving a capital outlay of £9000 results in net cash inflows of £4000 after intervals of 1, 2 and 3 years. If the discount rate is 10%, the NPV is as shown in Table 2.3 and so the project is financially viable.

Discounted cash flow — internal rate of return

The *internal rate of return* (IRR) method follows the same principles as for determining the NPV, but instead of determining the NPV given a specific discount rate r the IRR method seeks to find the discount rate r which gives an NPV of nil. Whereas NPV is expressed in money terms, IRR is determined as a percentage. In the preceding example, the IRR works out to be approximately 16%.

Readers are reminded that this is only a brief summary of capital investment appraisal methods. Actual appraisals require not only the inclusion of appropriate costs and revenues but may also be affected by general inflation, specific price changes, taxation and grants. Working capital investments should not be ignored. For further information see the reading lists given at the end of chapters 2 and 5.

Appendix 2.2. Forms specifying information required for project sanction
Capital investment proposal
Project no. ...

Part A (to be completed by sales department)
A1. Is this a continuation of an existing project?   Yes/No
    If so, state existing project number.
A2. Is this proposal a renewal of a previous proposal   Yes/No
    which was abandoned or rejected?
    If so, state previous existing project number and reasons for
    renewing application:

A3. Brief statement of sales requirements including minimum per-
    formance specification, national and international specifications,
    type testing and approval requirements:

A4. Indication of desirable product selling prices. Clearly state what
    units are included in the product for the prices quoted.

A5. Who are the principal competitors? What are the technical,
    marketing or price advantages associated with the product
    covered by this proposal?

A6. When is the product required for marketing?
A7. What is the product life span?

39

A8. What is the market for the project?

Year	Total market		Company share		
	Overseas	UK	Overseas	UK	Total

A9. Estimated product launching costs.

Year	
Extra sales effort	
Handbooks and brochures	
Advertising	
Exhibitions	
Total	

A10. Will the introduction of this new product increase or decrease the sales of other company products? Give details.

A11. *Marketing approval*
    Product Group Sales Manager   Date
    Marketing Director   Date

Part B (to be completed by Engineering Department)
B1. Brief statement of how requirement specified in A3 will be met.

B2. Statement of design characteristics including performance tolerances and margin over minimum sales performance specification.

B3. Does this proposal:
(*a*) Extend existing product range?   Yes/No
(*b*) Utilize existing company patents?   Yes/No
(*c*) Result in a patentable product?   Yes/No
(*d*) Risk infringing patents?   Yes/No
(*e*) Require additional specialist staff?   Yes/No
(*f*) Require additional specialist plant?   Yes/No
(*g*) Involve significant advance over current
in-house technology?   Yes/No
B4. Estimated development costs.
(*a*) Project evaluation and prototype stage.
Number of prototype equipments to be made. ...

Year	Eng	DO	Manufacture	Materials	Total

(*b*) Preproduction stage including preparation of manufacturing drawings and field trials.
Number of preproduction models to be made ...

Year	Eng	DO	Manufacture	Materials	Total

(*c*) Production and post development services including preparation of technical literature and manufacturing test specifications.

Year	Eng	DO	Manufacture	Materials	Total

41

(*d*) Total development costs.

Year	Eng	DO	Manufacture	Materials	Total

Total

(*e*) Recommended contingency ... %

B5. *Engineering approval*
     Chief Engineer   Date
     Technical Director   Date

Part C (to be completed by Production Department)
C1. Detail any additional plant or machinery required to manufacture this product and its cost.

C2. Estimated production costs.
     (Product must be to same build as specified in A3)

     Batch size
     Materials
     Bought-in-components
     Manufacture labour
     Assembly labour
     Testing
     Packing, including material
     Total cost
     Unit cost

C3. Estimated contingency ... %
C4. Comments on proposed product.

C5. *Production approval*
    Production Engineer   Date
    Production Director   Date

Part D (to be completed by Finance Department)
D1. Financial summary

	Years				
	0	1	2	3	....
Statistical information					
Tonnage sales					
Revenue per ton					
Operating costs per ton (excluding depreciation)					
Profit per ton (excluding depreciation)					
Profit calculation					
Revenue					
Operating costs					
Depreciation					
Taxation payable					
Profit before tax					
Add: depreciation					
Less: tax allowance on capital expenditure					
Taxable profit					
Tax payable at ... %					
Cash flow					
Profit before tax					
Add: depreciation					
Investment grants					
Less: capital expenditure tax payable working capital increase					
Net cash flows					

D2. Financial returns.
     Cash flows discounted at 25%

	Expected	−10% sales volume	−10% sales price	+10% operating costs
Cumulative cash flows Net present value				
Payback period				
Internal rate of return				
Return on capital Capital employed				
Profit before tax				
Return on capital before tax				

D3. *Financial approval*
     Management Accountant   Date
     Financial Director   Date

Part E. Proposal approval
Project approved for development, subject to periodic review in
accordance with standard development procedure.

Managing Director   Date

Distribution
Managing Director
Marketing Director
Production Director
Technical Director
Chief Engineer

3 Planning the planning

Planning is the link between the decision to proceed with a project and the consequent activities employing engineering and other specialists on its development, design, procurement, construction, start-up and commissioning. In this chapter the planning decisions that have to be made by the investor in a large project such as those in the chemical or power industries are discussed, but most of the principles stated apply also to contractors and firms or organizations in other industries. The objectives should first be defined, particularly to assess the value of time. There should be clear statements of policy to specify for example how plans shall be agreed, how contractors will be selected, and how changes to design or plan will be authorised and controlled. The resulting plans should be used to govern the timing of the use of resources and be an effective basis for control from the start of the work on a project.

Planning is like choosing a route on a map: we look for ways of getting to an objective, choosing from alternatives depending on the resources we can use and the value of speed. We can also see alternative parts of a route to use where we foresee difficulties or find as we proceed that conditions are not as predicted. The results of planning should be 'programmes' or *plans*[1] stating when to start and to finish every activity or group of activities we expect to require, with decisions on how each is to be carried out and who is responsible for it.

The more complex the project and the division of the work amongst groups of people and specialist firms, the greater the need for planning in advance to specify how everyone's contributions fit together and to anticipate how problems in one part may affect others. Planning has become increasingly valuable to achieving success in engineering project management. Controls of the timing or cost of their work have not always been enthusiastically welcomed by engineers, compared with their primary interests in design, development and other technical activities, but the network techniques of planning now available are attractive to many because they are methodical and based upon logic.[2] Indeed, there has been enthusiasm in developing networks and computed processing of numerical detail to the extent that care is needed to utilize what is sufficient for a project and to avoid using systems too elaborate to be effective.

The main objective of planning is to make the best use of time. Planning of a project should therefore commence early, even at the start of the feasibility studies. The detail can be evolved stage by stage, particularly during design, but before that some attention to planning can save time that becomes much more expensive to try to recover later.

Development of a plan

The initial formulation of an agreed plan is only a starting point for control. Key dates affecting many people can be decided early and resources reserved. Contractual time limits can also be set at the start, but while completion dates may be retained throughout a project, the timing of many activities can change considerably. This does not necessarily indicate bad planning or bad project management. On the contrary it can indicate sensible adjustment to changing needs or unforeseen problems, utilizing 'float' available in the agreed plan.[3] Revisions may also be required because of the demands of other projects.

Planning must not be regarded as a once-only exercise carried out at the start of a project. It should be seen as a continuing process, so that at any point in the work the users can see how the demands on them fit into meeting the objectives of the project. The objectives may also alter. Financial rates of interest have fluctuated in recent years, so affecting the accumulating cost of the capital investment during a project, and changes in demand and competition can affect the commercial or public value of completing a project in the planned time. The plan should obviously be revised accordingly, at the same time as adjusting it to meet problems or to take advantage of activities that are ahead of predictions. Whatever happens to the timing of individual activities, the most important requirement is that everyone concerned should know as soon as possible how their work is affected. This means that plans should be kept up-to-date regularly and issued in a form which is easy to understand and clearly indicates changes.

This philosophy of developing and up-dating the planning is frequently misunderstood. To the inexperienced observer it may seem ridiculous that when activities are late the plan is modified so that everyone is on time again. But planning cannot force things to happen. It can only state what should happen, and it is then the project manager's task to make things happen as planned.

Developing the plan should also be seen as a means of saving time. A positive approach is called for to ensure that once a plan is produced it is not regarded as the best that can be achieved. Throughout any project where time matters the plan should be subject to critical examination with the objective of further reducing the duration if possible.

The continual development and improvement of a plan does not necessarily suit the managers of groups participating in a project or responsible for ordering work from other organizations. Any of these will want to have dates fixed as soon as possible. Some intermediate targets or 'key dates' therefore should be decided and not changed without careful consideration even if float becomes available.

Responsibilities for planning

There are alternative ways of organizing the reponsibility for planning a project:

- A central planning section, not directly responsible to the project manager, can plan it.
- One or more members of such a planning section can be temporarily allocated to a project manager.
- The planning can be left to the project manager.
- The planning can be left to the groups or individuals contributing work for the project.

Each of these will work. Each has its merits, and the best will depend upon the complexity and urgency of the project.

The last alternative has the attraction that people are responsible for planning their own commitments, but it has no-one studying the project as a whole, independently of their own section of the work. There may also be a lack of experience in planning, but these disadvantages may be unimportant if the problems are not complex or if one group is responsible for most of a relatively small project.

Clearly, when a project manager is appointed he should study the needs of his project as a whole. He should take part in the planning decisions right from the start, though his other responsibilities as the project proceeds may not leave him time to do the planning in detail.

Leaving the planning to a specialist section results in the advantages that it can coordinate the planning with other projects, be independent of other commitments and cultivate expertise in planning techniques. It can also vary its attention to any one project as needs change. The disadvantage is that its plans may be regarded by others as 'planners' plans' and a demonstration of planning skill and techniques, especially if not prepared in consultation with the project manager and each group employed on the project. The project manager must avoid the temptation to leave the planning to the planning section so that he can get on with technical or other 'more important' things.[4]

These comparisons show why the most common choice is the combination of a project manager directing the policy for a project and a central planning section providing a service to all.

Phases of planning

One can plan to plan a project in two phases, the first being a study avoiding detail that is adequate for estimating the earliest possible completion date and establishing intermediate targets. This phase may be called *coarse-scale* planning. It need not be accurate, even if required as part of the decision whether to proceed with the project at all. Typically at this stage the scope of work will only be partly defined, and so the activity durations on the programme will be regarded with varying levels of reliability. These uncertainties can be accommodated in the process of project evaluation by the addition of an appropriate allowance on the project duration commensurate with the assessed accuracy of the data.

It is important that the derivations of all time estimates are carefully recorded for future reference, comparison and control purposes at this preliminary stage as well as in the subsequent detail phase of planning.

The availability of rare resources should be considered, especially if the project is to be built in a developing country, but optimization of the use of resources cannot be studied until the date for proceeding with the project is decided.

The second and continuing phase of planning a project therefore consists of studying dates and resources with the people involved and examining the detailed logic to determine the best sequence of work. It is no longer sufficient to use broad-scale descriptions such as '*erect structure* ' and '*install plant*'. These two groups of activities can overlap, so that the detail needs to be stated to show how activities depend upon others, the economical use of resources needs to be studied and a basis for monitoring progress established. The more detailed the plan the easier it is to assess progress. It is this phase which continues throughout the project, particularly to decide on the use of float time in allocating resources required for several projects.

Uncertainties

Plans should be agreed as achievable and realistic by those responsible for controlling the various activities or groups of activities on a project. It is not so certain how the word 'realistic' should be interpreted. Every activity cannot be given allowance for disasters such as strikes, exceptional weather, illness or material failures that may affect it, otherwise the plan will be a slack one and the benefits of planning and control never achieved. Conversely, a plan which ignores the complexity of activities, unpredictable deliveries of materials, the dates of holidays, etc., is not realistic.

Records and statistical data of performance on comparable previous projects are the usual starting point for deciding the time to be allowed for many activities, adding as 'contingencies' amounts of time to anticipate delays which may be caused by uncertainties or difficulties not encountered previously but now envisaged. The effective use of past-performance data does, however, require knowledge of its reliability and, in particular, whether the performance was good, bad or indifferent; there is always the risk of perpetuating poor performance by accepting previously achieved durations as 'realistic'.

If no performance data are known for an activity such as the first-time attempt at a research task or the development and design of novel equipment, a tentative estimate is needed drawing on the best judgement available. A range of estimates can be collected and a representative figure calculated statistically. Assuming a symmetrical combination of psychological[5] and physical probabilities, one method for this which is used with PERT planning[6] depends on obtaining three estimates of the time required:

a   the value of an 'optimistic' estimate, defined as one which has only a 1 in 10 chance of being bettered

m   the 'most likely' duration, in a considered judgement

b   the 'pessimistic' estimate, one which has a 1 in 10 chance of being exceeded.

From these the representative best figure is calculated as

$$(a + 4m + b)/6$$

One of the criticisms directed at network methods of planning is that their validity depends on the accuracy of the figures used and that it is impossible to make worthwhile estimates for these in the early stages of a project. This criticism would be valid if the first plan produced was regarded as the one and only one but, as stated earlier, a first plan using the best figures then available should be regarded as only the starting point. It is valuable in indicating the 'critical' path, the sequence of activities that limits the total time for completion of the project. Once this is known, the critical activities can be considered in more detail, re-examining the times for them obtained from uncertain information and studying the value of saving time by applying more resources or perhaps improving the method of work.

Time—cost optimization

Ideally, the speed of carrying out each activity for a project is optimized according to the value of time and to achieve the continuous or otherwise most economical use of all the resources employed on it.

Experience shows that this ideal is impracticable in most industries because of limited resources, the needs of other projects, the uncertainty of numerical information available for planning and other multiple influences that affect the duration and cost of activities.[7]

Partial optimization is practicable, and is commonly practised by studying the value of speeding groups of activities on the critical path and plotting how regular would be the use of any inflexible or expensive resources.[8] Adjustments can then be made to avoid immediate or large irregularities in the proposed use of these resources. Starting from the first planning for the project, the time allowed for each group of activities is reviewed against the cost of time in the way shown in Fig. 3.1. Combining the fixed and variable costs in this way illustrates these choices for the duration of critical activities:

- *minimum cost* — the duration for least cost, the optimum if speed of completion of the project has no commercial or other financial value

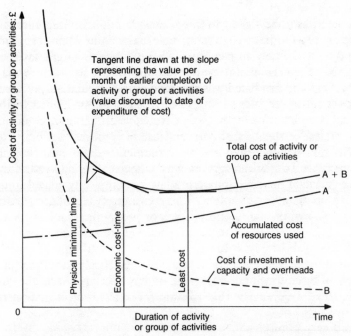

Assuming that the work content is known the investment in the capacity to carry it out can be chosen by equating the predicted duration and the predicted total cost.

Fig. 3.1. Choosing the capacity for carrying out an activity or group of activities

51

- *minimum time* — the duration for carrying out the work at the fastest speed, usually set by physical limits such as space, crane speeds, time for an undercoat of paint to dry, etc.

- *optimum cost-time* — the duration costing more than the minimum by the amount equal to the value of the time saved, but discounting the latter sum over the period between expenditure and pay back.

From any re-examination of the planning which makes it possible to predict a reduced duration for the project, a new critical path may emerge for scrutiny and possible shortening. The activities that appear to have a small amount of 'float' and which might be termed 'sub-critical' can of course become critical if the original critical path is shortened.

Freezing the plan

There has to be a limit to this reconsideration and replanning. The plan has to be 'frozen' at or before the point when trying to improve it is likely to use much of the time this might save.

This is then the plan to be put into use. It can be given formal approval by management, though of course some dates may have to be reconsidered later because of commercial incentives to achieve earlier completion or because of unavoidable difficulties, requiring reappraisal of the critical path and use of resources.

When forecasting their project's completion date, most project managers will declare an appropriate contingency period in addition to the planned project duration to allow for completely unavoidable and unpredictable difficulties. This contingency allowance would not be shown on the 'working' plan or programme and, indeed, it would be expected to reduce progressively to zero as the project proceeds and the risk of disasters recedes. It should not of course be used to absorb or permit delays due to inefficient working (in-house or by contractors), changes of design, shortages of resources, etc., all of which are within the control of the project manager.

Planning techniques
Networks

It is widely if not universally accepted that network techniques are the most effective for planning complex projects. Most readers will be familiar with the *arrow diagram* or *activity-on-arrow* form of network, the technique for determining critical paths that is described in many textbooks.[2] An alternative form is the *precedence diagram*. This is described in Appendix 3.1. It is a technique that appears to have gained popularity in many parts of the world because of the advantages discussed in Appendix 3.1.

Bar charts

An older technique is the *bar chart* in which activities are represented by 'bars' of length proportional to their duration and the plan is drawn to a scale of time so that the user is able to see at a glance the required timing and sequence of activities, and can readily use the chart for marking and monitoring progress. Unfortunately this system of planning presents problems for the planner — it is not easy to represent exactly complex inter-relationships between dependent activities in detail, so bar charts tend to be drawn in rather broad scale with overlapping activities and, of course, lacking any float or critical path information. In basic form their use for project management is therefore rather limited.

The advantages of bar charts and networks can be combined once a network has been analysed and the results calculated, by presenting the results in a bar chart form complete with float.

Presentation of critical path information

There are three basic methods of presenting detailed critical path information to the user:

● on the network itself
● in tabular form
● in bar chart form.

Each has its merits and uses:

● *On the network.* This is the normal method when carrying out 'manual' calculations but becomes rather tedious for regular updating when repeated redrawing as well as recalculation is required. It has the advantage of retaining the logic of the network for all to see and especially when the facility for automatic network drawing by computer is available, the network method remains a viable option. The main disadvantage would seem to be the size of the diagram, often occupying several sheets and presenting difficulties in handling as well as in following the critical and non-critical paths.

- *Tabular or digital information.* Probably the most common method of presentation and ideal for computer sorting of data from large networks. Fig. 3.2 shows a typical example and here the results have been sorted to present only electrical and instrument activities and in *ij* order. The main advantage is the clear display of important information: earliest start and finish dates (here in calendar format) as well as total float. Tables of this sort can be varied or extended to include other useful information such as free float, resource requirements, names of individuals responsible, cost, etc, for each activity shown.

9:09 AM FRI., 25 OCT., 1985

OVERALL SUMMARY PROGRAMME 16334
****

I	J	DESCRIPTION OF ACTIVITY	START	DUR	FINISH	TF
ELECTRIC & INSTRUMENT						
300018	300019	COMPLETE MANUFACT&DELIVER CONTROL SUITE	24JUN85	48	6JUN86	-3
300019	300021	INSTALL & TEST CONTROL SYSTEM	9JUN86	9	8AUG86	-3
300021	300023	CONTROL CABLING TERMINATIONS & L.A.T's	11AUG86	23	30JAN87	-3
300031	300033	AMENITIES INSTALLATION	7OCT85	23	28MAR86	10
300033	300035	AMENITIES FINAL FIX	31MAR86	6	9MAY86	10
300037	300039	AMENITIES SYSTEMS TESTS	12MAY86	10	18JUL86	10
300051	300053	START MAIN TRAY/TRUNKING PROCESS BLOCK	2DEC85	6	24JAN86	7
300053	300055	CONT. MAIN TRAY/TRUNKING PROCESS BLOCK	27JAN86	9	28MAR86	7
300057	300059	CONTINUE INSTALLATION DESIGN	17JUN85	36	7MAR86	10
300061	300063	IN-CELL INSTALLATION	7APR86	19	15AUG86	6
300065	300067	GROUT AREA INSTALLATION	8SEP86	8	31OCT86	21
300069	300071	DRUM HANDLING INSTALLATION	4AUG86	14	7NOV86	0
300073	300075	STREET LIGHTING INSTALLATION	7OCT85	15	31JAN86	12
300075	300077	LIGHT & SMALL POWER INSTALLATION	3FEB86	15	16MAY86	12
300077	300079	MISC. ELECTRICAL SERVICES INSTALLATION	19MAY86	8	11JUL86	12
300079	300081	ELECTRICAL SERVICES PAT's	14JUL86	12	3OCT86	12
300085	300087	MANUFACTURE ELECTRICAL PLANT	24JUN85	25	13DEC85	15
300089	300091	ELECTRICAL PLANT INSTALLATION	16DEC85	10	7MAR86	15
300093	300095	LTF CABLING INSTALLATION	27JAN86	13	25APR86	8
300095	300097	LTF CABLING & TERMS	28APR86	15	8AUG86	8
300097	300099	ELECTRICAL PLANT PAT's	11AUG86	12	31OCT86	8
300101	300103	SUB 45 INSTALLATION	2DEC85	7	31JAN86	17
300105	300107	ENERGISE PD 1	3FEB86	4	28FEB86	17
300111	300113	MANUFACTURE MISC INSTRUMENT HARDWARE	24JUN85	39	4APR86	9

Fig. 3.2. Overall summary programme

- *Bar chart format.* Typical examples of this method produced by line printer are shown in Fig. 3.3. This shows the same information as Fig. 3.2 but the 'pictorial' presentation of the bar chart using a time scale facilitates more rapid comprehension by the user, especially when assessing the significance of progress reports for each activity and, for example, the effects of delays and the utilisation of float. A complete bar chart print-out of all a project's activities in order of earliest start by total float can provide a very convenient method of presenting the project plan for the use of the project manager. A vertical line or cursor can be drawn each week or reference period to indicate 'time now' in order to follow and record progress on the plan. It is important to ensure that free float is identified as well as total float in order to utilize the float correctly.

Time-scales

The units of time chosen for planning a project should depend upon the total duration and the frequency of control. For a large project, months may be the best units for the initial planning, and then the detail later studied in weeks. It is possible to start by calculating durations rather than dates, and then change over and consider seasonal effects, holidays, etc., when choosing the starting date for a project. Computer programs used in complex planning will calculate similarly and may be arranged to present the results on any form of time-scale required, including calendar date format.

Calendar dates are ideal for recognition but confusing to use in manual calculations because of the irregular lengths of months. To overcome this a 'semi-calendar' language can be used counting the weeks through the year; in this, the first week of 1989 is written 89·01 and the last week is 89·52. Adding and subtracting durations is then relatively simple as these examples show:

$$88·20 + 7 = 88·27$$
$$90·03 - 6 = 89·49$$
$$88·25 + 41 = 89·14.$$

Computer programs are available which use this format. Personal diaries can be used by all the people involved which include week numbers. In offices and on site the number can also be displayed week by week. As there are not exactly 52 weeks in a year the final

OVERALL SUMMARY PROGRAMME 16334
****

9:54 AM FRI., 25 OCT., 1985

C=Critical i.e. TF=0 or Neg
X=Non Critical i.e. TF>0
-=Positive Float
V=Today's Date

Each Character Represents 1 Week

					1985					1986									
I-Node	J-Node	Description of Activity	TF	Dep	Oct	Nov	De	Jan	Feb	Mar	Apr	May	Jun	Jul	Aug	Sep	Oct	Nov	De

ELECTRIC & INSTRUMENT

I-Node	J-Node	Description of Activity	TF
300018	300019	COMPLETE MANUFACT&DELIVER CONTROL SUITE	-3
300019	300021	INSTALL & TEST CONTROL SYSTEM	-3
300021	300023	CONTROL CABLING TERMINATIONS & L.A.T's	-3
300031	300033	AMENITIES INSTALLATION	10
300033	300035	AMENITIES FINAL FIX	10
300035	300039	AMENITIES SYSTEMS TESTS	10
300051	300053	START MAIN TRAY/TRUNKING PROCESS BLOCK	7
300053	300055	CONT. MAIN TRAY/TRUNKING PROCESS BLOCK	7
300057	300059	CONTINUE INSTALLATION DESIGN	10
300059	300063	IN-CELL INSTALLATION	6
300061	300065	GROUT AREA INSTALLATION	21
300069	300067	DRUM HANDLING INSTALLATION	0
300073	300075	STREET LIGHTING INSTALLATION	12
300075	300077	LIGHT & SMALL POWER INSTALLATION	12
300077	300079	MISC. ELECTRICAL SERVICES INSTALLATION	12
300079	300081	ELECTRICAL SERVICES PAT's	12
300085	300087	MANUFACTURE ELECTRICAL PLANT	15
300089	300091	ELECTRICAL PLANT INSTALLATION	15
300093	300095	LTF CABLING INSTALLATION	8
300095	300097	LTF CABLING & TERMS	8
300097	300099	ELECTRICAL PLANT PAT's	8
300101	300103	SUB 45 INSTALLATION	17
300105	300107	ENERGISE PD 1	17
300111	300113	MANUFACTURE MISC INSTRUMENT HARDWARE	9
300113	300115	INSTALL FIELD INSTRUMENTS	9
300117	300119	INSTRUMENT CC's INSTALLATION	8
300119	300121	INSTRUMENT CC's TERMS	8
300121	300123	INSTRUMENT SYSTEMS LAT's & PAT's	8
300131	300133	MANUFACTURE MONITORS	9
300133	300135	COMPLETE DEVELOP & TEST MONITORS	9
300135	300141	INSTALL&TEST PROCESS DETECTORS&MONITORS	9
300137	300139	INSTALL & TEST H.P INSTRUMENTS	9
300143	300145	PR/CONTRACT DETECTORS	31
300145	300147	MANUFACTURE DETECTORS	31
300149	300151	INSTALL & TEST CCTV's	9

Fig. 3.3. Overall summary programme

week is usually 'extended' to include the additional day or days, thereby accommodating to some extent the statutory holiday.

A similar form of numbering can be used for other time-scales, such as a day—hour basis for planning the maintenance or commissioning of equipment. Numerical time-scales which start at zero representing the start of a project and progress to completion are not recommended for large projects or in any organization where more than one project is being handled. Otherwise confusion arises from the different time reference being used on different projects for the same week or day.

Monitoring

The system of monitoring progress to compare plans with achievement should be designed according to what result is wanted. Monitoring can be arranged to produce accounts of the use of time. It can be used to replan to overcome changes, delays and errors and as a basis for management. For the latter it is not sufficient to know that an activity is running late. It is also necessary to know whether action is being taken to complete it on time. The most important information is the answer to the question 'How long will the activity take to complete?' Suppose that an activity in the plan should now be under way and is being monitored:

Activity:	'design steelwork'
Estimated duration:	5 weeks
Work content:	10 drawings
Resource allocation:	2 designers, averaging 1 drawing per designer-week

and that a progress report at the end of week 2 for this activity states that only two drawings have been completed.

The report might state either '2 drawings complete' or '20% of drawings complete'. In either case it could be deduced that the work is now taking twice as long as anticipated and therefore that the total duration of the activity will be 10 weeks. The major concern is when the next activity can begin, and as this consists of meeting a key date for placing a contract for the steelwork, all the drawings are required. In fact it is possible to come to several different views as to how this may be effected and what to do. An alternative deduction from the report of progress is that the activity is 1 week behind, and that the total duration will therefore be 6 weeks.[9] Or perhaps it is the two most difficult drawings that have been completed, and the remainder will be completed within the planned period. Some experience in that work is needed to judge. The only clear way to assess the true position is to obtain a responsible estimate of the time to be taken to complete the drawings. Additional information in terms of the number of drawings completed is certainly of interest, but contributes only a guide to performance and to the reliability of statements on the time required to complete the work.

Computation

In detail, many activities vary from the plan, some finishing early and others late without affecting the ultimate result but altering the distribution of float and making some more nearly critical. Regular up-dating of the plan and inclusion of this detail is useful both to check progress and to make the best of all changes. Electronic data processing is here most valuable, to produce results in time to be used.

Alternatively, the progress of each activity can be recorded on a bar chart print-out with a bold vertical line being added to indicate the real time date of collecting the progress information and markers indicating the status of each activity relative to this date. In this way the chart becomes an effective basis for reviews of progress and remedial actions and the frequency of update computations can be much reduced.

Progress reporting

Information on which to judge the progress of activities can be obtained by several means. An obvious one is to obtain it directly from the people responsible for each activity. They can send in regular returns on a standard form reporting on all their activities or they can be asked to report only on those activities not going to plan — the principle of 'reporting by exception'. Alternatively, they can report verbally when they are visited at regular intervals.

The advantages of obtaining the information from visiting those responsible are that uncertainties in statements can be discussed and personal contacts are maintained between them and the project team. By this means, information on the rest of the project can also be passed around and cooperation generally encouraged. It should need less paperwork than the alternative means, but perhaps its greatest advantage is that the progressor will under-stand the situation as seen by all concerned and be able to hear about the state of services and support for the work.

Clearly, these advantages are difficult to achieve if the work for a project is divided amongst widely separated groups of people. The telephone and teleprinter are common means of overcoming this, but lack the capacity for clarifying uncertainties or including 'fringe' information. Regular meetings drawing together represen-tatives of all the critical or potentially critical activities are the other expedient. To be effective these should be based on prior written or oral reports and statements of actions in hand to overcome diffi-culties, so that people's time is used as efficiently as possible. The meeting is to check on information and action. For maximum effectiveness and to avoid delay the meetings should be frequent and regular. Monthly is a typical arrangement for projects lasting a year or more, but it is logical to change the frequency at dif-ferent stages in a project. Logarithmic intervals have been used. Although meetings have the obvious advantage of promoting liaison, they have the disadvantage of requiring people to leave their work, and problems tend to be saved up for the next meeting rather than tackled directly by the people concerned. Avoiding this and using time at meetings well demands a knowledgeable and determined chairman. It is usually therefore a task for the project manager or his boss.

Standard progress forms

Although people are not always willing to give information on forms, the use of standard answers obtained this way combined with a style of management that achieves personal links is the common arrangement for projects involving many firms. The value of using a standard form is that consistent information should be obtained, it involves the least use of time, and the frequency of reporting can be varied and made intense on critical detail. More care is also taken by people having to write and sign a statement of progress and problems than is usual if reporting by telephone.

Management by exception

If reports are required only when the people engaged on an activity decide to state that it is going wrong, there is a very human tendency for them to do this only after they have taken time and

59

resources in trying to overcome the problem as they see it. Illness and omissions can also cause the report to come too late to the project manager or planners who are in a position to see if the problem is critical and warrants additional expenditure.

However, reporting only on problems is economical on everybody's time and leaves the responsibility undivided. In practice, it is always used for the detail of work, although clearly there would not be much progress if interruptions for sharpening a pencil or answering the telephone had to be reported on a form. The managers involved should agree to what extent the non-critical activities or groups of activities should be reported on regularly. This must depend upon organizational experience of the people involved, the uncertainties in the plan and the potential competition for the resources for other projects.

Control decisions

Given an up-to-date policy on the cost and time for completing a project, there remain many decisions on adjusting detail in the regular updating of a plan. Sometimes some non-critical activities have to be delayed in order to make resources available to more critical ones, or for some other project. More often the problem is to accelerate critical or near critical work. The decisions needed are much the same at any stage of a project, though they vary in complexity and cost. A few examples are now discussed drawn from situations encountered in capital investment such as a chemical manufacturing project using the investing company's resources for research, development, project definition, engineering and start-up, but employing contractors to carry out the manufacture and installation of equipment and structures.

Extended development

Even if the research required prior to deciding to proceed with the project had been completed satisfactorily, there can be problems in the subsequent development work and a progress report indicating, for example, that pilot-plant trials might need to be extended. Experimental work is probably the most unpredictable activity in a project. Statistical calculations of the sort already described are appropriate in these circumstances, using a range of estimates of possible durations to allow for the uncertainties.

If the forecast duration is seen to be extending, the choice is to delay all subsequent stages and thus the completion of the project, or to overlap development with design and thus accept the risk that some of the development will be unsuccessful and the dependent design work will have to be repeated. At this stage in a project only a small proportion of the total cost has been spent and during the remaining time to completion there may be changes in its commercial value. The tendency therefore is to accept such an early delay rather than spend money in accelerating development or design. This often turns out to be a wrong policy. The scale of expenditure needed to overcome the delay at that stage is relatively small, and cheap compared with buying back the same amount of time during the much larger scale of material activities that follow design. The alternatives are to overlap design with development, or perhaps even better to cancel the development work by changing to an existing process and a proved design.

Delays in design information

In design, the decisions made are more dependent on each other than in all the subsequent stages of work until the start-up of equipment. Some parts of a project are relatively easy to design, but planning may be necessary to make sure that the difficult problems upon which they depend are tackled first and that the prior decisions have been made. The orderly handling of information is important in employing the varieties of specialists and services whose expertise is required. Achieving a planned work-load also entirely governs the cost of running a design department.

Although float may be available, people are not machines. They are adaptable, but at the risk of losing their enthusiasm and concern for detail. The importance of delays or changes in information for designers is sometimes exaggerated, but perhaps only those who work with them can see the frustration and other effects that follow waiting or wasted work.

Discipline is needed in the project team, process engineering and others responsible to ensure that information flows into design on time and in the right sequence. Inevitably, some problems will arise such as in the supporting development work, but it is in the initial stages of design that the pattern of progress is set for the rest of the project.

Procurement delays

The purchaser's freedom to make decisions is more limited when concerned with delays or the apparent risk of delays in design, manufacturing or other work ordered on contractors and sub-contractors, as the resources employed are beyond direct control. Conflicts of interests are always possible as a result of any division of responsibilities.

This does not mean that a customer and his supplier must always be in dispute, but they do have different objectives in balancing costs against the progress and quality of the contracted work. Their financial interests are discussed in later chapters. Here the concern is with problems arising at the first indication of delay to achieve an agreed or implied speed of work.

Though the supplier accepts the obligation to achieve delivery, the customer is concerned whether this is likely to be achieved. The customer is therefore likely to wish to have information on how this will be done, to see the contractor's planning, the allocation of resources and know who is responsible. Ideally, the customer should be satisfied that a contractor has the technical, financial and managerial capacity before placing the order on him. Past performance and current commitments are both important. Differences between contractors' competing tender prices are usually small compared with the cost to the customer of a poor performance in completing the contracted work.

Given detailed knowledge of a chosen contractor's planning and progress, an indication of delay during his work may be treated as a problem to be solved together. Discussion should reveal whether there are difficulties with a sub-contractor, a delay in materials, labour problems, overloading of manufacturing or other capacity, failures in testing, or a lack of anticipation of any of these and other risks. Solutions must be sought from a starting point which asks the supplier contractually responsible 'What are you doing to make sure we get this item on time?' before asking 'How can we help you to get it to us on time?' Important here is our knowledge of the cost of their delay in terms of completion of the project and the physical or psychological effects on the other work. The project manager must decide whether it is worth spending anything on speeding the delivery, e.g. for overtime or shift working, selective delivery of critical items, or specially rapid transportation of the completed work.

The first step is to look for means of controlling and overcoming the slippage without extra cost to the customer. An extreme alternative is for the customer to cancel the order and place all or parts of it elsewhere. This needs to be considered quickly in order to take a decision before all the time for the activity has elapsed. If a lack of materials is the problem of a contractor or sub-contractor, the customer's stores may be able to help. Or, as in overcoming a development problem, a contractor's delay may possibly be avoided by altering or simplifying part of a design or specification. Contractual obligations are obviously altered if any of these latter alternatives are used. To anticipate these and other consequences of changes that may be needed, the project manager and others involved should be able to rely on the monitoring system giving them early warning of the possibility of contractors' delays in critical or inflexible activities.

Construction and start-up

By the time a capital project is under construction, there may be little float or flexibility for overcoming delays resulting from the foregoing stages. If the planning and control have been adequate, the required completion date should still be secure. If much of the float has been used up and completion may be delayed, special endeavours may be needed to recover the time, depending upon the objectives of the project.

The earliest possible start-up may be wanted, in order to begin selling for instance, so that for a chemical project the key event is the time when materials can be put through the manufacturing process. Construction and start-up should therefore be planned together, as this may show that many activities for the completion of the construction or the correction of faults in it are not critical. From much earlier, the preparations for start-up may have been critical — the preparations including activities such as the selection and training of operators and supervisors, preparation of testing and commissioning instructions, establishing safety rules and starting the trial of equipment and sub-systems.

Management reports

As general management does not have the time or perhaps the patience to read the detailed 'status' of all the projects under study or sanctioned, selective reporting is required. To make it easy to

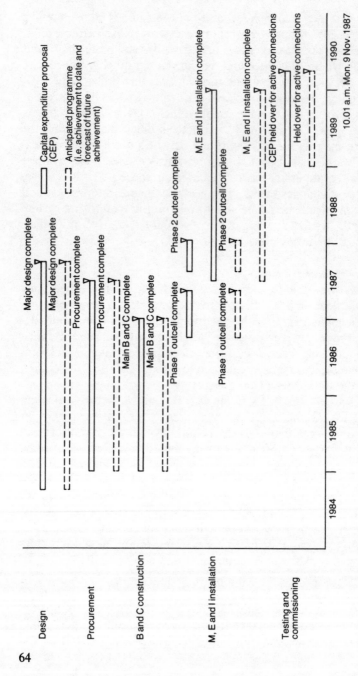

Fig. 3.4. Summary programme indicating general project status in form convenient for rapid assimilation by top management

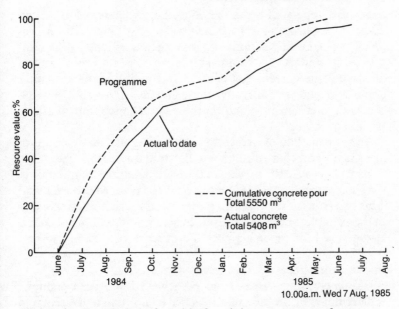

Fig. 3.5.   Trend chart for critical activity — concrete placement

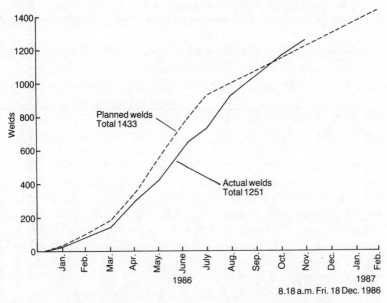

Fig. 3.6.   Trend chart for critical activity — pipe welding

compare a report with the previous one, a standard format can be used, requiring only brief accompanying statements on progress, problems and actions affecting critical activities or contingencies in budgets. A summary programme is a useful way of displaying the current status of a project and, using computer graphics, a variety of attractive presentations are possible. Fig. 3.4 shows a typical example and, in this case, a happy state of affairs for all concerned!

Another method of presenting easily read information on progress is a trend chart of the form illustrated in Figs 3.5 and 3.6, so named because the progress information marked on it indicates the general trend towards or away from the planned achievement. This can be used for reporting important or critical activities, as in the examples shown, or the project as a whole, and can of course also be used for reporting cost and other resource expenditure.

Factors for success in planning

Ultimately, the degree of success achieved in project planning is determined by the closeness of actual completion to the required or planned time. This may well provide a measure of the skill and determination of the project manager but due recognition must be given to the many independent factors that can influence the results.

Elements of luck, for example, appear in all activities. Plans should be prepared with sufficient awareness of the consequences of both good fortune and bad to enable some limits of confidence or accuracy to be declared when predicting completion. The accuracy should improve as the project proceeds and periods of uncertainty recede into the past, but it is not uncommon to encounter some particularly complex problem at the very end of a project. Care and experience are needed to identify the risk areas and assess the possible sources and consequences of trouble. Overall, one might expect the good luck to balance out the bad on the 'swings and roundabouts' principle but this may not be good enough for projects which are very sensitive to changes in duration. If so, it is appropriate to consider the more sophisticated PERT approach using three-time estimates and computed probability forecasts for completion dates.

Other factors which affect project timing can be associated with the performance of people. When the people concerned are outside the area of direct organizational control by the project manager, their level of performance may depend less upon motivating factors associated with commitments to the project than independent environmental or perhaps political factors. The successful performance of 'functional' managers then becomes a primary requirement, although much may depend upon the effectiveness of the project manager in stimulating progress by simple expedients such as personal contact, frankness, and good communications.

The demands of other projects competing for the use of critical resources often introduce the need for a higher level of decision making affecting perhaps different areas of business: the aim should be to evaluate the effects of delay carefully before pronouncing on the 'priorities' and avoid if possible bringing even the less important projects to a complete standstill.

Perhaps the most important factor for success in planning and control of a project duration is the extent to which the project manager and everyone working on the project are committed to achieving this success. The overall responsibility should be clearly defined and to ensure this commitments should not be shared, but in the final analysis the results will reflect the contributions of many and it is in the interests of all that significant contributions are identified and acknowledged.

Notes
1. In this chapter the word 'plan' is used to mean a list, drawing or computer print-out showing the dates or durations for activities. We have avoided the common alternative 'programme' because of possible confusion with a computer program. 'Schedule' is also not used here, it having a slightly different common meaning in contracts.
2. A summary of the precedence method of network analysis is given in Appendix 3.1. which follows. For details on planning methods see among many others:

Lockyer, K.G. *Critical path analysis*, Pitman, London, 1982.
Mulvaney, J.E. *Analysis bar charting*, 2nd edn., Kumarian Press, 1980.
Thompson, P.A. *Organization and economics of construction*, 2nd edn. McGraw-Hill, 1989.
Neale, R.H. and Neale, D.E. *Construction planning*, Thomas Telford, London, 1989.

British Standards Institution. *The use of network techniques in project management.* BSI, London, 1981 and 1984, BS 6046.

3. 'Float' is the time available for an activity or a group of activities in excess of the amount needed.
4. Responsibilities for the control of projects are discussed further in chapter 7.
5. For a discussion of psychological probabilities in decision making see Cohen, J. and Christensen, I. *Information and choice.* Oliver & Boyd, Edinburgh, 1970.
6. 'PERT' signifies Program Evaluation Research Technique, one method of network analysis. For this and the statistical theory for estimating uncertain durations see the books listed in note 2.
7. See, for instance, the large number of papers presented at international conferences on networking.
8. Resources which are 'inflexible' in that their availability or capacity cannot be rapidly or economically changed include: some specialists in design offices, project engineers, heavy vessel fabricators, site cranes, testing instruments and often the simple matter of space for installing equipment, cabling, etc.
9. In planning or progressing any activity, do not assume that results are produced linearly as time elapses. Indeed, it is common experience that 90% completion is easy to achieve, but the last 10% takes much more work, i.e. time is not linear. Perhaps a slow start and a slow finish is most typical for any activity, a group of activities or a complete project, following the S curve form of the rate of expenditure illustrated in chapter 5.

Appendix 3.1. Precedence diagrams for critical path analysis
Drawing a network showing the logical sequence of activities for a project and noting estimates of their expected durations provides the information necessary to identify the critical paths and sort out the less critical activities. One common form of network is the *arrow diagram*, or *activity-on-arrow* system, with each activity or group of

Table 3.1. Precedence list

Ref.	Activity description	Duration	Dependencies
A	Vessel installation	—	—
B	Pipe fabrication	—	—
C	Vessel lagging	—	A
D	Pipe installation	—	A, B

activities represented by an arrow whilst circles or 'nodes' represent the events at the start and finish of activities.

The alternative is the *activity-on-node* or *precedence* system. This is based on nodes representing activities. Lines are then added to connect the activity nodes in their logical sequence. The start can be made from a list of activities to be planned showing their dependence upon preceding activities. The completed table shows precedences and durations. Table 3.1 shows part of such a table. Fig. 3.7(a) illustrates the same information in the form of a precedence diagram and Fig. 3.7(b) is the corresponding arrow diagram. The comparison demonstrates the advantage of simplicity which the precedence system provides. In particular, the 'dummy' activity (2−4) is not required. The form of diagram shown in Fig. 3.7(a) is also helpful to people familiar with process flow sheets, manufacturing route charts, computer flow charts, decision trees and organization charts.

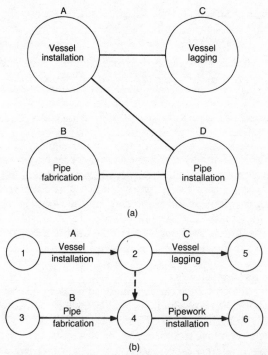

Fig. 3.7. Network examples prepared from data in Table 3.1: (a) precedence or 'activity-on-node' form; (b) arrow diagram form

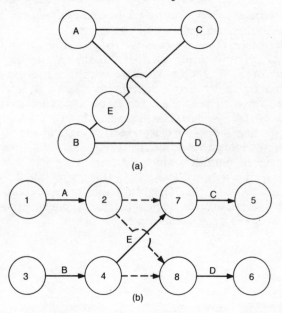

Fig. 3.8. Modified version of network showing the effect of introducing an extra activity E: (a) precedence form; (b) arrow diagram form

Modifications

The need from time to time to modify the planning of a project to change the logic or add or remove an activity may rquire redrawing a section of a network. As an example, say it is necessary to introduce another activity E into the networks shown above where E cannot start until B is complete and C depends on the completion of A and E. Fig. 3.8(a) shows that the precedence diagram can be modified by adding the E node between B and C. To modify the arrow diagram requires re-drawing, to appear as shown in Fig. 3.8(b).

Numbering systems

In the precedence system the activities can be identified by reference numbers which can be retained despite changes in the detail or logic. The above comparison showed that the modified arrow diagram required new reference numbers for activities C and D, whereas no change of node references was necessary in the precedence diagram. This is valuable in avoiding the need to alter the references in lists and tabulated information.

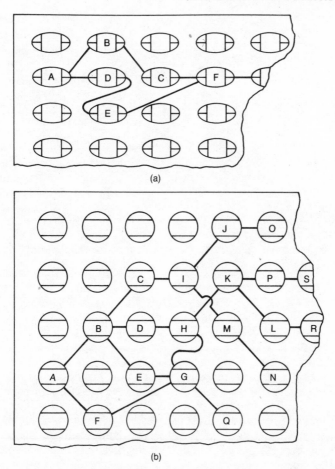

(a)

(b)

Fig. 3.9. Pre-printed node sheets: (a) for manual calculation using node form as Fig. 3.10(a); (b) for computer calculation using node form as Fig. 3.10(b)

Pre-printed node sheets

The planner can study the dependencies of activities for a project by working on a pre-printed sheet of nodes as shown in Fig. 3.9. This is particularly useful in exercises in planning and replanning. The spacing and size of the nodes is designed to promote neatness and clarity which are retained despite changes of mind in pencilling in the lines showing dependencies. Alternatively a rubber stamp of the

71

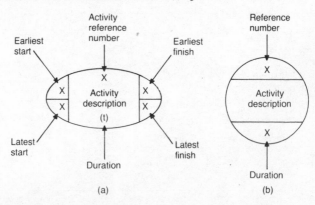

Fig. 3.10. Typical node forms: (a) for manual calculation — spaces are provided for inserting descriptive and calculated data; (b) for computer calculation — minimum space provided allowing for mainly descriptive information

node can be used where required on blank paper, but care should then be taken to leave some space between nodes for later additions or changes of logic.

The form of node symbol can be designed to suit the user. For manual calculations giving all the data on the diagram, a larger node is required than for diagrams where the results will be calculated using a computer. Types of nodes used successfully are shown in Fig. 3.10. In the type for use in manual calculations, note the position of the earliest and latest start and finish times, as these will be referred to later in discussing the method of calculation.

Overlapping

Of particular importance during the early planning stages of a project is the need to represent satisfactorily the overlapping of dependent broad-scale activities. The precedence diagram lends itself conveniently to the method whereby the amount of overlap is indicated by inserting numbers on the appropriate dependency lines. In Fig. 3.11 two overlapping activities of durations 10 and 8 weeks are shown in bar-chart form (a) and in precedence form (b). The numeral 5 indicates the degree of overlap in both cases. A negative number would be used to indicate a 'delay' between the end of one activity and the start of another as illustrated in Fig. 3.12. Note that systems using the opposite notation (negative numbers for overlaps and positive for delays) are understood to exist so care may be needed to avoid confusion when using proprietary software for precedence networks.

Method of calculation for precedence diagrams

The method is best described by example. Fig. 3.13 shows a small network of four activities in which the durations have been added and

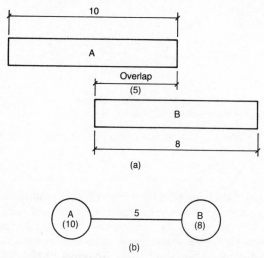

Fig. 3.11. Overlapping dependent activities: (a) bar chart form; (b) equivalent precedence form (number on dependency line indicates degree of overlap)

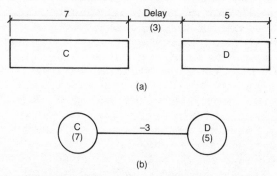

Fig. 3.12. Dependent activities showing delay or negative overlap: (a) bar chart form; (b) equivalent precedence form (delay shown by negative number on dependency line)

73

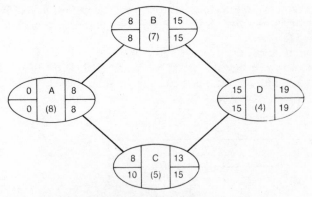

Total float is the difference between earliest and latest starts or finishes. Hence, critical path is A–B–D

Fig. 3.13. Simple precedence network showing results of manual calculation

the calculated starts and finishes entered. Assuming a starting time of zero and time units in weeks, the calculation proceeds as follows.

If, say, 0 is entered as the earliest start of A, by adding the duration 8 weeks the earliest finish of A is entered as week 8. Activities B and C cannot therefore start earlier than week 8 and this is inserted as the earliest start for both B and C. Similar calculations are carried out for B and C. As with activity-on-arrow calculations, the highest value of the earliest finishes of preceding activities is entered as the earliest start for the next activity: this means that the earliest start for D is week 15 (earliest finish of B) rather than 13 (earliest finish of C). The reverse calculation proceeds in conventional manner and in this case the lowest value of the latest starts is entered as the latest finish of a preceding activity, e.g. the latest finish for A is selected from the latest start of B (week 8) and the latest start of C (week 10).

Float is easily calculated. Total float of an activity is the difference between the earliest and latest starts (or finishes) and, of course, the critical path is identified by the sequence of activities with minimum total float. Free float is the minimum value of the difference between earliest finish time and the earliest start times of succeeding activities. In the example (Fig. 3.13), total float and free float for activity C is 2 weeks. Activities A, B and D form the critical path.

It should be noted that 'events' such as key dates can be included in a precedence network by entering them as activities with zero duration. In this way 'event' reports can be generated if required.

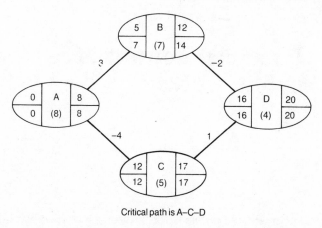

Critical path is A–C–D

Fig. 3.14. Precedence network example with overlaps and delays showing results of manual calculation

The method of calculation using overlaps and delays is similar, as the next example (Fig. 3.14) shows. It will be seen that the earliest start for B is now arrived at by subtracting the overlap duration, 3, from the earliest finish time of A, 8. The earliest start for C, however, is calculated by subtracting the negative overlap, i.e. by adding the delay value to the earliest finish of A. The reverse, or 'backward pass' calculations require overlap values to be added and delay values to be subtracted, e.g. latest finish of C = latest start of D (16) + overlap (1) = 17. Latest finish of B = latest start of D (16) − delay (2) = 14.

Most computer programs for critical path analysis were originally designed for activity-on-arrow input, but now most appear to offer optional facilities for precedence input. This means that there is scope for the user of precedence to develop large detailed networks and to derive fully computed analysis with the minimum of manual effort. Particularly important in this respect is the further advantage of being able to develop input data in the form of a 'precedence list' (as Table 3.1) without the need for network drawing. If a diagram is required to facilitate discussion for instance, systems using graph plotters are available that automatically print out the network.

4 Financial control of public works

The development of a public works project is governed by political decisions and guided by established procedures. A number of organizations, committees or departments are usually involved in the progress of a single project. Consequently, particular attention must be given to communication between these parties and the project staff must have sufficient authority to ensure that the problems of design and construction are overcome before they cost extra money or delay completion.

The time between the initiation of feasibility studies and the commissioning of a project is likely to be many years and the resulting facility may be operated and maintained for several decades. Various problems not normally encountered in commercial projects of relatively short duration are therefore likely to affect a public works project:

- Continuity of staff involvement is rare and it is therefore difficult for one engineer to emulate the forthright approach to project management witnessed in the commercial environment of, say, the offshore industry.[1,2] There is, however, much that can be done to drive a project to a successful conclusion.
- Forecasting the demand for the facility is particularly difficult.
- In the contractual situation, the engineer employed by a public authority is greatly influenced and sometimes restrained by the pressures and traditions of public accountability.

Consequently public works projects which are excellent in engineering terms may prove frustrating to those involved with their development and may also be disappointing to the user, the community, as the long awaited facility may prove inadequate on completion. Many projects have been perceived to be failures by Government and the community due to cost and/or time overruns or inability to meet an increased demand. The balance between success and failure is sometimes delicate and these same projects could well have been acclaimed as successful had the project manager resisted pressure to trim realistic cost estimates, paid more attention to programme or been less inhibited in his perception of future demand.

There is much that can be done to improve project development and implementation. In this chapter the opportunity for the promoters[3] of public works to control projects is considered and ways in which they may play a more positive role in their management are suggested.

Project management by the promoter

Project management is concerned with the efficient use of resources: for the promoter of a project the principal resource is money. Although the increasing complexity and size of capital projects, high interest rates and the shortage of capital have increased the need for improved financial control by promoters, several factors complicate the decision-making necessary to achieve effective control in the public sector, such as:

- the division of responsibilities in public authorities between finance, engineering and other departments
- the separation of design and construction
- the high incidence of design changes and delays and inadequate contractual machinery for their systematic evaluation
- a general ignorance of time's significant effect on both construction costs and on the use of capital.

The power of a promoter to influence the outcome of a project varies at different stages of its evolution. The scale of his investment is decided following feasibility studies. At that stage the design office's decisions control the cost of individual elements. Once contracts are signed the promoter is committed; thereafter, his interest is best served by co-ordinating the work of all parties involved in construction and commissioning and by exerting control over design changes.

It is therefore apparent that effective control of the physical

77

realization of a project relies on the realistic definition of objectives, careful planning of design, construction and commissioning, acceptance of a realistic budget, and regular monitoring of the promoter's actual commitment against the targets set by his plan.

Planning is a continuous process; unexpected difficulties will arise and it is common for design changes to be incorporated as construction proceeds. The current plan must then be revised to produce a new optimum solution corresponding to the changed situation or requirements. Departure from the agreed plan, once design and construction are under way, will probably result in increased cost or a reduction in return from the investment, or both.

Other factors affecting the viability of a project may also change during the design and construction phase. In particular, further information is usually obtained to improve the prediction of the demand for the service or product. The cost of the project should also become more precisely known. Overall control of the investment can therefore only be achieved by regular reappraisal of all aspects of the scheme and could well result in a change in the timing or extent of further development of the project.

Time and money

All these variables are likely to influence both the time scale and the finances of a project. A design change may not only increase the material cost of some element of work but may also cause a delay in construction and commissioning. The delay may be alleviated by the provision of additional resources on site, again incurring additional cost. The change may in turn affect the efficiency of the completed scheme. All are likely to change the flow of money to or from its promoter.

Despite reforms in administration, time and money are still frequently considered separately in many public authorities, sometimes by separate departments; they should be closely related in order to assess the true position on a project or any individual contract at any point in time. The plan, whether it be for a project as a whole or some element of its development, comprises a programme (the time forecast) and an estimate (the consequent financial forecast).

The plan for overall appraisal of a public works project is based on long-term predictions. The plan for construction involves departments, utilities, suppliers and contractors, all of which are susceptible to change and must therefore be flexible so that alternative courses of action are presented for decision by the project manager when change occurs.

The project

This text is mainly concerned with the appraisal and engineering phases of projects, by which the facility is provided. The reader is encouraged to consider the time scale of the three phases before proceeding to consider individual aspects of project management.

In many public works projects appraisal and reappraisal will be repeated several times as each project waits for funding in the national or regional programme of works. Thirteen years has recently been quoted as the average period which elapses between acceptance in the programme and completion of a section of motorway in the UK. The engineering phase will be relatively short, design and construction jointly spanning perhaps two to five years, and the promoter will then be responsible for operation and maintenance of the facility for many years.

The various aspects of project and contract management is now considered in more detail.

Appraisal

The promoter commits himself to investment in a project on the basis of the appraisal completed prior to sanction. The appraisal must be realistic and identify all risks, uncertainties and potential problem areas.

All alternative patterns of project development should be thoroughly explored at this conceptual stage of project development. One unfortunate effect of competition on consultants' fees has been to reduce the time which can be devoted to this process and reduce the likelihood of finding the optimum solution.

The uncertainty associated with project selection has been discussed in chapter 2. Problems of forecasting traffic flows, water consumption or passenger figures are particularly severe in major infrastructure projects due to the long lead-time before construction and the difficulty of expanding the facility once it is in use. Examples of projects which illustrate the difficulties of prediction of demand are the M25 motorway which proved inadequate when finally completed, or of the excess capacity of the Keilder water scheme due to the decline of the industries it was built to serve.

79

The only practical way in which the risk can be reduced is to design such projects for phased development, thereby delaying investment in expanding the initial facility until the demand is confirmed — as illustrated in the *New Water Scheme* example below.

There will frequently be conflict between the economist and the engineer and between the promoter and the Government. The economist and the Treasury will both wish to minimize the initial cost of the project, the former to show a better return on the investment. Such pressure tends to inhibit realistic forecasting of future demand and time and time again ensures that good range estimates are replaced by optimistically low figures.

It is perhaps salutory to recognize that the more successful a Government's economic policy, the more likely its predictions concerning use of the infrastructure are likely to be inadequate! Economic growth will stimulate growth in many areas.

The realism of forecasts will, of course, improve if the lead-time for public works projects can be reduced. This can only be achieved by greater investment in the infrastructure and by streamlining the lengthy approval procedures prior to sanction. Some considerable reduction of the period between conception and completion of projects is fast becoming a political necessity in Britain and would offer probably the single most significant contribution to the provision of an adequate national infrastructure.

A promoter and his project manager can frequently reduce the risk of completing a project which fails to meet the demand by pressing for some sensible provisions to be made for future expansion of the facility. The duplication of a motorway in the future with all the associated disruption to the community may be unthinkable; construction of a two-lane carriageway but with wider bridges and space for a third lane could be prudent and economically justifiable.

Construction projects of all types are also subject to other risks and uncertainties. These should be exposed and the implications evaluated and considered during appraisal. They will have a big influence on project viability and are most likely to be reduced, transferred or removed if thoroughly analysed at an early date.[4]

Other constaints and problems, particular those affecting detailed design and construction, will be exposed by early consideration of the method and programme of construction. Preliminary works which will reduce the disruption and nuisance to the public during the main construction phase may be identified and a case made for award of a separate advance works contract. Early planning may also highlight activities which affect the timing of award of a contract — such as the diversion of a river during a period of low flow, avoiding road closures at peak holiday periods or the seasonal nature of earthworks construction.

Use of discounted rate of return in investment decisions for commercial projects has been mentioned in chapter 2. While the great value of discounting techniques is recognized, care is needed when applying them to projects with long operational lives. Significant future costs — of maintenance, replacement or decommissioning, can conveniently be 'lost' or disguised at the appraisal stage when they count for little in discounted figures. They are very real and significant 30 years later![5]

Project objectives

Promoters often have a number of objectives for undertaking a project. These may be commercial, reflect the perceived needs of society and/or have political overtones. Specific project management objectives must be compatible with the overall objectives and should be clearly formulated early in the appraisal stage of project development.

The dominant considerations must be fitness for purpose of the completed project and safety during both the construction and operational phases. Thereafter cost, time and functional performance form a minimum set of values from which the primary objectives will be drawn. The potential for conflict between these objectives, as problems arise during project implementation, is obvious.[6] The disasters which beset the Montreal Olympics Stadium — a prestige public works project of novel design with an unrealistic budget and a fixed time constraint — offer salutory reading to all promoters and their project managers.[7]

To try to avoid these problems, the objectives of a project should be ranked in terms of their relative importance. Tolerances must also be specified — as range of acceptable variation in performance, float in the programme and contingency allowances in the estimate. The greater the perceived uncertainty, the more flexible these criteria must be. Unclear or ill-defined objectives will have a detrimental effect on decision making and progress. The responsibility and the authority to use contingencies should be allocated

81

to the project manager as it is essential for him to know what has been used and what remains at any point in time.[8]

Thereafter the monitoring of progress and performance against these objectives will determine the need for replanning, revision of estimates and changes in project scope and specifications. In public works projects minimum cost is frequently, and sometimes wrongly, accepted as the dominant objective. When inadequate contingencies have been defined and problems arise, the stringent financial constraints can only be met by reductions in project scope, quality or safety. This approach is prevalent in public works projects,[9] is disruptive, has an adverse effect on morale and is likely to lead to public dissatisfaction with the project however well the remainder of the work may be completed. If is far better to expose the uncertainties and potential problems, allow for them in the estimate and adopt realistic objectives in the first place.

The fact that the promoter and the community do not see any return on the investment until the project is commissioned suggests that timely completion should always be a prime objective.

Misunderstandings and mistakes are prevalent in the early stages of development of construction projects if objectives are not clearly defined and effective liaison between the various contributors is lacking. This can be particularly serious in the conceptual design which should be rigorously reviewed to ensure compliance with the promoters' objectives. Regular audit of a project by a person or organization external to the project team has been found to stimulate economy and anticipate errors.

Statutory approvals

All construction projects, private or public are sensibly subject to approval by Local Planning Authorities. In a relatively small and crowded country great benefit has been derived from adherence to well-defined policies for local and regional development such as preservation of the green belt. The democratic right of an individual to influence the development of the environment in which he or she resides is also appreciated. The time and expenditure devoted to the democratic process of public enquiry and appeal has, however, become excessive in recent years and adds significantly to the undesirably long gestation period of public works projects. The democratic process of Public Inquiry and Planning Approval for a new and necessary source of water may take seven years.[10] Delay of this magnitude can result in hardship to consumers and additional cost.

Cost estimating

Estimates of cost and time should be prepared and revised at many stages throughout the development of a project or contract. They are all *predictions* of the final outcome of the job and the degree of realism and confidence achieved will depend on the level of definition of the work and the extent of risk and uncertainty. Consequently, the accuracy of successive estimates should improve as a project or contract is developed. The most important estimates prepared are probably for a project, at sanction, and for a contract, at tender. It is at these points that the promoter and then a contractor become committed.

These predictions can be influenced by factors peculiar to the particular project under consideration. Location, logistics, weather, availability and capability of resources and market factors may all affect the final price. Estimates must therefore be compiled with the circumstances of the project clearly in mind and all assumptions, uncertainties and exclusions should be stated. Ideally, any estimate should be presented as a most probable value and a tolerance, together with a range of less likely values to emphasise that it is an estimate. It is important to realise that the precise value of a specific single-figure estimate made at an early stage of the project or contract is most unlikely to be achieved due to the uncertainty of civil engineering work.

Estimates for public works projects in industrialized countries such as the UK are frequently derived from data banks of historical unit rates. Ideally the data should be from a sufficiently large sample of similar work in a similar location and constructed in similar circumstances. The figures must be systematically corrected for the effect of inflation.

The unit-rate technique as traditionally used in UK construction contracts does not demand an examination of the programme or method of construction and the estimate is frequently compiled by the direct application of historical 'prices'. It therefore does not require an analysis of the real costs of the work, neither does it encourage consideration of the peculiarities, constraints and risks affecting the particular project. Although consideration of a detailed programme is not a necessity when compiling an estimate from

83

unit rates, it is strongly recommended that one is prepared. This will be particularly valuable in identifying problems of construction which will go undetected if the technique is applied in a purely arithmetical way. It will also be required for cash flow prediction.

The operational technique is by far the best method of evaluating uncertainties and risks, particularly those likely to cause delay. This is the fundamental estimating technique in which the total cost of the work is compiled from consideration of the constituent operations or activities defined in the construction method statement and programme and from the accumulated demand for resources.[11] Labour, plant and materials are costed at current rates. The advantage of working in current costs is obtained. Compilation is relatively painstaking and time-consuming compared with other techniques, but when preparing an operational estimate the estimator will gain a realistic appreciation of the risk and special circumstances of the project.

Preparation of an operational type of estimate for each major construction contract, based on the information available to tenderers, prior to bidding is strongly recommended as it offers the following advantages:

- The adequacy of the tender documents is checked.
- Construction problems associated with design are exposed.
- The promoter can check that all his contractual commitments can be honoured (e.g. access to site) prior to award of the contract.
- The implications of risk and uncertainty can be studied and the relevant provision of contingency determined.
- The estimate gives a reliable basis for the assessment of tenders.
- The knowledge of costs and programme will assist the promoter in management of the contract and particularly in the evaluation of claims and variations.

Planning

The need for thorough and continuous planning and replanning has been stressed in chapter 3.

In his planning a promoter must take a broad view of the project and aim to co-ordinate design, construction, commissioning and subsequent operation and maintenance. The success of a project depends greatly on the management effort expended in the early stages of development. Interaction of contractors, access, statutory requirements and public relations must all be considered.

Co-ordination of the activities of statutory authorities deserves special attention in public works projects as the diversion of pipes and cables is a frequent source of delay and of subsequent contractual dispute.

Because of the uncertain nature of construction work it should be expected that the plan will change. It must therefore be updated regularly and quickly if it is to remain a guide to the most efficient way of completing the job. The programme should therefore be simple — so that updating is straightforward and does not demand the feedback of large amounts of data from busy men — and flexible, so that all alternative courses of action are obvious.

Contract strategy

In the traditional approach to the procurement of public works projects, design is undertaken by the promoter or a consulting engineer in an office remote from the construction site. Construction contracts are awarded to specialist contractors, normally on the basis of the lowest price submitted in competitive tender. The majority of the construction contracts are of the admeasurement type.[12]

The increasing diversity of promoters' objectives has however meant that the established systems of working and the associated model conditions of contract are not always appropriate. No single uniform approach to contractual arrangements can be specified or advocated. A number of alternative strategies are available and each contract should be formulated with the specific job in mind.

A wide range of contractual forms and arrangements have evolved during the past decade and consequently the definition of an effective and realistic contract strategy for the procurement of the works is a key function of the project manager in the early stages of any engineering project.[13] The strategy should define the organizational and contractual policies chosen for the execution of a project. The development of a contract strategy should consist of a thorough assessment of the choices available for the implementation and management of design, fabrication and construction. A pattern of interrelated decisions is required which seeks to maximize the likelihood of achievement of the important project objectives.

The decisions taken during the development of a contract strategy affect the responsibilities of the parties; they influence the control of design, construction and commissioning and hence the co-ordination of the parties; they allocate risk and define policies for risk management; and they define the extent of control transferred to contractors. Therefore they affect cost, time and quality.

The majority of the contracts used for the procurement of public works are likely to remain price-based, in which the final contract price is derived from rates submitted by the selected contractor in his tender. As the degree of risk, uncertainty or novelty increases it may be necessary to select a cost-based contract in which actual costs are reimbursed together with a fee for overheads and profit.

In the building sector various forms of management contracts are increasingly popular. In these systems an external organization, the management contractor or construction manager is employed specifically to manage and co-ordinate design and construction on behalf of the promoter. This approach is frequently adopted to achieve early completion of the project by 'fast-tracking'[14], i.e. by overlapping and integrating design and construction. It is most appropriate for construction which can be split into a series of well-defined contract packages, each of which is awarded immediately the relevant design is completed. The management contractor is normally employed on a cost-reimbursable basis and although the construction contracts are of the familiar admeasurement form, it is important to realize that the allocation of risk between the parties may be considerably changed. Success is heavily dependent on the quality of the contractor's management team.[15]

The level and form of the promoter's involvement in management of the implementation phase of the project will be greatly influenced by the contract strategy selected and is likely to vary with each different approach.

The following issues are of particular relevance when determining that strategy:

- The procedures must be compatible with the promoter's declared objectives. The relative importance of quality, safety, economy and timely completion must therefore be agreed, and appropriate tolerances or minimum standards specified for all four. The number of secondary objectives should be kept to a minimum.

- Responsibility for co-ordination of design, fabrication/construction and commissioning must be clearly defined. The flow of information between different work packages may require the introduction of procedures for interface control, particularly in 'fast-track' projects.
- It should be recognized that timely completion is not the essence of a competitive price-based contract. If early or timely completion is to be given priority then either adequate incentive must be introduced or a fast-track policy adopted.
- Rigorous assessment and allocation of risk. All parties will benefit from reduction of uncertainty prior to financial commitment.[4]
- The likely extent of change and variation to the work allowed for in the contract documents is frequently underestimated. If not viewed realistically this could lead to selection of the wrong strategy or to the premature issue of contract documents.
- In most of the model forms of contract the clauses relating to programme are weak and may require redrafting to facilitate effective project management.
- Most contractual claims relate to the delay or disruption of contractors' activities. Effective procedures for the adjustment of the contract price in such circumstances should be established in the contract documents. Use of method-related charges for the purpose is likely to be most effective when they are closely related to the agreed programme.[11]

Contract management

The final contract price will frequently exceed the tendered price due to the uncertainties associated with construction activity. There are many ways in which a promoter may influence the final price including:

- by ensuring that the work to be performed is adequately defined in the tender documents, and that the form of contract employed is suited to the particular contract
- by fulfilling his obligations and checking that the contractor's intentions agree with his requirement before the contract is signed
- by restricting design changes and co-ordinating the operations of all parties to prevent delays.

The definition of the work in a contract, the form of contract, methods of measurement and valuation are related. All should be chosen to suit the objectives of each project. The criteria for the selection of the form of contract should be the amount of change and interference with the contractor's operations expected between tender and final account. The approach will obviously be different for a power station and rural road scheme. The former is large and complex, design and construction proceed concurrently and may extend over a time span of many years, and there are numerous interfaces between contracts; the probability of change and delay is high and target contracts may be appropriate.[16] A rural road scheme may well have been redesigned several times whilst awaiting grant approval and the works will therefore be precisely defined and quantified in the tender documents; a single contractor is employed. Nevertheless, the average increase in value of civil engineering contracts utilizing bills of quantities has been shown to be 10.5%.[17]

There is an understandable desire by those responsible for the promotion of public works to see construction started immediately a project has been sanctioned. The tender documents not only define the commitment required from the successful contractor, but also commit the employer to fulfil his obligations under the contract. Many contracts go to tender too early. It is still common to find that demolition is outstanding, land has not been purchased or easements not negotiated although the contract has been awarded. Many contractual claims that plague the industry and take up so much time arise because promoters and their engineers have not fulfilled their obligations at the time of tendering. This situation can be avoided if the logical process of project planning is applied across interdisciplinary boundaries and all relevant activities focus on acceptance of the tender.

The tender submitted by a contractor is usually derived from a method statement of construction based on an interpretation of the contract documents. The timescale of this scheme is important to the promoter for it determines the flow of information to the contractor, may affect the timing of other contracts and is the basis of valuation of contractual variations. The promoter should require the favoured tenderer to furnish a method-statement or programme before the contract is signed so that the relationship between price and programme is firmly established. The facility to recognize the potential for and the consequences of disruption and/or delay will again aid the control of design changes and speed the evaluation of any variations and claims.

Effective site supervision is another important element of the promoter's management role. Quality assurance systems alone are not an adequate substitute for the presence of diligent and experienced resident staff.

Maintenance and urban renewal

In the UK and most industrialized countries an increasing proportion of the national public works budget must be devoted to the refurbishment or renewal of the decaying infrastructure.[18]

The strengthening of an ageing earth dam, renewal of water mains and deep sewers or the maintenance of a road are all likely to generate unique technical problems and will almost certainly cause disruption to the community. In the future, far more attention must be given to the planning of these works — in the broadest sense — and the traditional objective of economy will become secondary to the need to reduce inconvenience and/or nuisance to the public. To do this successfully two major changes in central and local government policy will be needed:

- a move from annual budgeting and cash limits to funding over periods of several years, with greater attention paid to life-cycle costs
- co-ordination of construction projects on a regional basis.

The introduction of lane-rental incentives to accelerate the refurbishment of motorways and the development and utilization of no-dig techniques for the replacement of sewers, pipes and cables are but early attempts to meet this change in objectives. Public opinion coupled with the need to prolong the existing infrastructure and ever increasing utilization and congestion on the roads may, for instance, lead to the use of more expensive but longer lasting surfacing materials in order to reduce the frequency of closures for maintenance.

Public works projects are currently undertaken to meet the requirements of a particular promoter with little thought of co-ordination with other projects. Thus a road may be opened up or obstructed several times in a matter of months for activities which could have been completed within a single period of disruption.

There are also numerous examples of traffic restrictions imposed on motorways concurrently with road works restricting routes which could otherwise be utilized as diversions. The establishment of Regional Project Planning Units, staffed by experienced and independent construction planners, to advise on the timing of all new construction, maintenance and refurbishment works is long overdue. For such units to be effective the collaborating authorities and utilities would need to be given greater flexibility in funding.

Cost models

Effective financial control of the promoter's investment in the project demands continuous consideration of cash flows as both the timing and magnitude of expenditure and predicted benefit will affect the demand for finance. It is therefore helpful to think of the plan as a time and money 'model' of the project. Such a model can be used to indicate realistically the probable financial implications of proposed or threatened changes before decisions are made in both the appraisal and engineering phases of the project. It will also give the promoter a feel for the degree of uncertainty associated with the project and this, in turn, should lead to consideration of ways in which the uncertainty may be reduced.[19]

The accuracy of the predictions depends upon the accuracy of the data provided. Realistic predictions of the time and money consequences of a decision are also dependent upon the correct definition of costs and revenues. If revenue is directly proportional to quantity of output or effort it must be calculated that way in the model; similarly, a resource cost which varies according to the time for which it is required must be so defined.

A library computer program called *CASPAR* has been developed and widely used by the author specifically for project appraisal and management by the promoter.[20]

Use of the model

The procedure for incorporating the time and money characteristics of a project into the model is simple.

As in planning, the total work content of the project is divided into a number of elements sufficient to achieve the desired accuracy of prediction and control, each becoming an 'activity' of specified duration or work content, with resource requirements and consequent costs and revenue. The timescale is in weeks or months and the project life, spanning appraisal, engineering and operation may extend over a maximum period thirty years. In the appraisal stage it is normal to work in months and the project is likely to be represented by a few large activities as illustrated in the *New Water Scheme* example below.

The time relationship between activities can be expressed in a precedence diagram (Fig. 4.1), which resembles a flow-chart and is the simplest form of network analysis. Individual activities may be assigned fixed start or finish dates but it is advantageous initially to impose the minimum number of restraints, thus giving flexibility and enabling the model to adjust the timing of activities to comply with the chosen optimizing criterion. Most resources, and certain changes such as overheads, will be of a general nature and may be used by a number of activities. These are represented by 'hammocks' which span the overall duration of the relevant activities. The total weekly/monthly demand for specific resources, such as design engineers, or a raw material, is predicted by accumulating the requirements of individual activities. Similarly, output of products may be forecast and their costs and revenues generated. The hammock facility may also be used as a restraint on the development. Where an upper limit is imposed on the availability of a particular resource, the program will adjust the timing of the associated activities to comply with this limitation.

All costs and revenues are assumed to be either fixed charges incurred at a defined point in time, time-related charges which are proportional to the duration of an activity or hammock, or charges proportional to quantity of work performed or output produced by an activity or hammock. For example, part of the operating costs and all revenues for the case study of a *New Water Scheme* used in Fig. 4.1 are defined per unit of production, whilst the cost of design staff is time-related and will increase should the design activity take longer than planned. Changes in output or work content will therefore produce a realistic statement of the effect on programme, cost and cash-flow.

The above data, initially representing the envisaged pattern of development, are assembled and processed to form the basic model in the standard computer program. The basic model can then be re-run with minor data changes to simulate changes in output, costs or prices, in the availability of resources, quantities of work included

Fig. 4.1 (below and facing page). Flow chart for cost model of project — New Water Scheme — showing the relationship between individual activities and all time restraints on the development (this chart is in the form of a precedence diagram of the type described in Appendix 3.1)

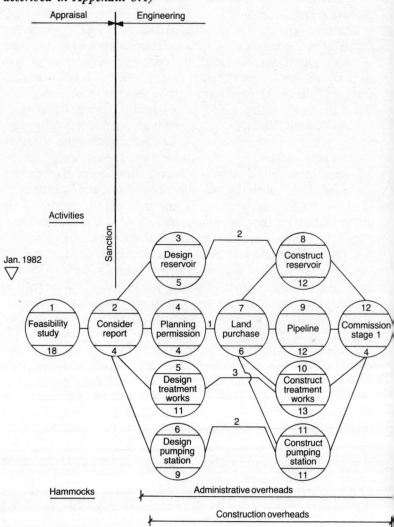

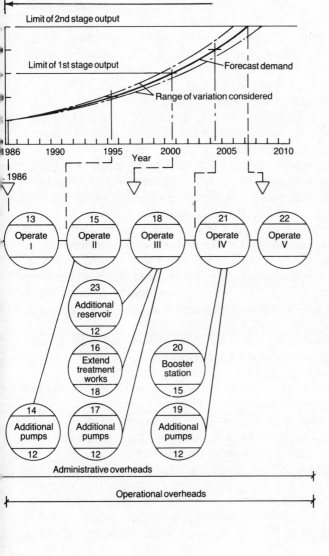

in the contract, different patterns of staging the project, or the effect of delays. Sensitivity analysis and probabilistic risk analysis can be generated by the change of any one factor or combination of factors, and will give an overall picture of the uncertainty associated with the investment.

As the project or contract evolves and more detailed information becomes available, individual activities may be easily subdivided and new activities introduced so that the investment may be regularly reappraised and the effect of changes in plans, design or expectations can be rapidly simulated to aid decisions by the project manager.

Control of a project — New Water Scheme

Use of the *CASPAR* model for the control of a project comprising a pumping station, pipeline, treatment works and terminal reservoir is now considered.

The evolution of the first stage of this scheme is initially divided into twelve activities and a precedence diagram, Fig. 4.1, has been drawn to illustrate the logic of the development. Any activity may be sub-divided, if necessary, at a later date.

In this simplified example it is assumed that the approvals and consents required during the appraisal phase will not cause undue difficulty and that a public enquiry will not be needed. All these preliminary activities have therefore been combined into 18 months of 'feasibility study'. For most public works projects these preliminary activities are closely linked and must be defined in detail as they are a prolific source of delays.

Demand for the product may be specified either as a sequence of activities, each defining a fixed output over a period of months, or as a single activity with a given continuous rate of growth. Sudden steps in demand can therefore be incorporated. Changes in the forecast of demand will affect the timing of subsequent stages of the development of the project. The program is designed to initiate the construction of such stages so that they are commissioned when demand reaches specified levels.

In this case the initial demand for treated water is predicted to be 25 Ml/day and the capacity of the first stage development is selected as 75 Ml/day with an ultimate capacity of 125 Ml/day. The best forecast of future demand shows that consumption will reach this figure in 2007. If operation is considered to the end of

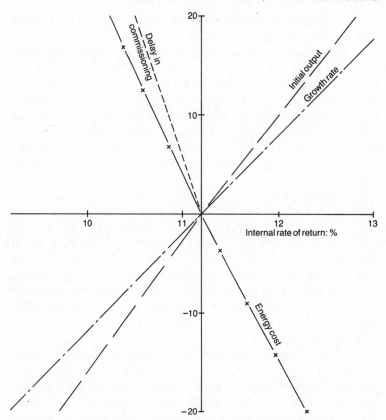

Fig. 4.2. Sensitivity analysis for New Water Scheme

2011 the rate of return is 11.2% and the maximum demand for capital £2.78 million. In this exercise both the growth rate of demand and the initial demand have been varied over a range of ±20%. The results of this sensitivity analysis are illustrated in Fig. 4.2 and are seen to produce an appreciable difference in the financial return. Delays in commissioning Stage 1 are also seen to have a significant effect on the financial viability of the scheme.

Similar simulations could be performed for a range of unit operating costs and revenues. Variations in engineering cost, cost of water treatment and the cost of energy were included in the original analysis but have been omitted from the diagram for clarity.

Alternatively, the model may be used to predict the real price of a unit of the product.

The relationship between delay in commissioning and the financial outcome of the project should be a major influence on the decisions of the project manager throughout design and construction.[21] For instance, the land agent or valuer employed for this scheme might consider that he could reduce the cost of land and easements by 10% if given an additional three months for negotiations. Simulation of this situation would show the project manager that, on financial grounds alone, this extension should not be granted.

The merits of alternative methods of financing the scheme have been considered separately in this example. The basic appraisal indicates that a positive return would be obtained over the selected period of operation if money were borrowed at an interest rate of less than 11.2%. The implications of the timing, size and nature of different loans can be examined by reference to the accounting procedures which are part of the standard output of the model and utilize the cash flow information generated by the interaction of time and money.

Models of this type are widely used in the private sector and in the water industry. They are simple to use and could well prove very effective in encouraging better management of public works projects. The model forms a link between all departments involved in the project. The facility to demonstrate the uncertainty associated with the project and also the consequences of indecision are of particular value to the project manager.

Conclusions

Constraints imposed by central government inhibit effective appraisal and management of many public works projects. Consequently the public's perception of a completed project may be disappointing.

Greater attention should be given to future long-term needs of the community when appraising such projects. A more realistic and imaginative view of future demand must be encouraged. The appraisal process should be accelerated to shorten the lead-time between project conception and completion.

There is urgent need for better co-ordination of all public works projects involving construction, maintenance and/or refurbishment in an area or region in order to reduce disruption in the community.

Promoters of public works projects should pay more attention to management of design and construction. Early consideration of the appropriate contract strategy, reduction of uncertainty, programme constraints and requirements is advised. Care in the appointment of contractors is also important.

In future, the current dominant desire for economy must be balanced by the need to satisfy the needs of the electorate. More money and resources must be devoted to development and refurbishment of the infrastructure and to minimizing the nuisance caused to the public whilst this construction work is proceeding.

Notes

1. Gaisford, R. Project management in the North Sea. *Int. J. Project Mgmt*, 1986, **4**, no. 1, 5–12.
2. Gregg, D.E. *et al.* Murchison project preliminary planning organization. *Proceedings of European Offshore Petroleum Conference*. London, 1978.
3. 'The Promoter' is the term used by the Institution of Civil Engineers in their handbook *Civil engineering procedure*. Alternatives also used are 'Owner', 'Employer' and 'Client'.
4. Perry, J.G. and Hayes, R.W. Risk and its management in construction projects. *Proc. Instn. Civ. Engrs*, Part 1, 1985, **78**, June, 499–520.
5. Project Management Group. *Severn tidal power: sensitivity and risk analysis*. UMIST, Manchester, 1980.
6. Neil, J.M. *Construction cost estimating for project control*. Prentice Hall, 1982.
7. Barnes, N.M.L. Human factors in cost control, *Proc. 5th Int. Cost Engng Congr.*, pp. 244–248. Danish Association of Cost Engineers, Utrecht, 1978.
8. Ninos, G.E. and Wearne, S.H. Control of projects during construction. *Proc. Instn Civ. Engrs*, Part 1, 1986, **80**, Aug., 931–943.
9. National Economic Development Office. *The public client and the construction industries*. HMSO, London, 1975.
10. Boddington, T.J. and Farrar, R.S. The promotion of the Meldon Dam in the Dartmoor National Park. *J. Instn Wat. Engrs*, 1975.
11. Thompson, P.A. *Organization and economics of construction*, 2nd edn. McGraw-Hill, 1990.
12. Wearne, S.H. *Civil engineering contracts*. Thomas Telford, London, 1989.

13. Perry, J.G. *Contract strategies for construction*. William Collins, 1990.
14. Wearne, S.H. Fast-track project direction. *Int. J. Project Mgmt*, 1984, **2**, no. 4, Nov., 240–241.
15. Hayes, R.W. *et al. Management contracting*. Construction Industry Research and Information Association, London, 1983, report 100.
16. Perry, J.G. *et al. Target and cost-reimbursable construction contracts*. Construction Industry Research and Information Association, London, 1982, report 85.
17. Figures from an analysis of bills of quantities included in *Civil engineering bills of quantities*. Construction Industry Research and Information, London, 1971, section 3.3.2.
18. Infrastructure Planning Group. *First report*. Institution of Civil Engineers, London, 1984.
19. Hayes, R.W. *et al. Risk management in engineering construction*, University of Manchester Institute of Science and Technology, 1986. Distributed by Thomas Telford, London.
20. Thompson, P.A. and Willmer, G. CASPAR — a program for engineering project appraisal and management. *Proceedings of Conference on Civil Engineering Computing, London*, 1985, vol. 1, 75–82. Civ-Comp, Edinburgh.
21. See example of the use of such models for project management in chapter 11 of reference in note 11.

5 Financial control in mechanical contracting

Contractors who are in business to supply capital plant usually have to offer a potential customer a tender quoting fixed prices for undertaking to design and make the plant specified, including the work of sub-contractors, etc. Often a contractor is also responsible for the erection of the plant at the customer's site, for testing, and for assisting in commissioning it. The size and complexity of major projects today have increased greatly a contractor's risks in estimating the costs of undertaking these responsibilities. In this chapter principles for establishing financial control of such contractual commitments are set out. Similar methods can be equally important to sub-contractors, customers or any organization affected by the flow of cash or the costs of changes during their work for a project.

Twin aspects of financial control

Financial control in contracting has two aspects, one static and the other dynamic.

The first consists of establishing accounting procedures to record costs, identify variances, ascribe their causes, and provide an up-to-date indication of the probable financial outcome of a contract.[1] This is mainly a job for accountants, but the mechanisms and purposes should be understood by all the people whose work is being monitored. This aspect concerns only the contractor doing the work, and not the client for whom he is doing it. To the latter the cost of the project is the value of the relevant contracts placed by him. He is not concerned with whether those contracts result in a profit or a loss for the contractor, but only to see that the contractor has not added to the client's costs by lateness or other causes.

Dynamic control consists of judgement and action to avoid variances. It demands action in time to anticipate and, if possible, avoid extra costs. This is the concern of all those responsible for any section of a contract. It is the practical and effective aspect of financial control. If applied rigorously, from day one of every contract, it will ensure that nobody spends money without first considering the consequences.

Static control
Accounting procedures
For present purposes, it is assumed that any contractor seeking to operate a system of financial control already operates an appropriate and disciplined system of costing and accounting. If that aspect is deficient or suspect, there can be no financial control.

Financial control begins before tendering, and finishes at the end of the maintenance period. Between these two points a contract must be under regular and disciplined review. Since static control is essentially a book-keeping exercise, it is imperative to have a simple, workable system.

The estimate
The basis of a good system starts with the estimate, the quality of which will depend on:

- the time available for tendering
- the contractor's previous experience at designing and instal-ling similar plant
- the complexity of the plant
- the ability of the estimators.

However good or bad the estimate may be, it must be so constructed that future expenditure can be monitored against it. There are, after all, only two principal reasons why contracts overspend; either the estimate was too low, or the prices paid for equipment and services were too high. There is in fact a third reason, that the scope of the project changed during its life, and the project manager was unable or too lazy to negotiate the recovery of the extra costs from the client. This third reason, however, has little to do with cost control *per se* — it merely indicates a management deficiency.

Thus it is essential to ensure that the final estimate (i.e. the one against which the project manager will work) is built up of elements that will in due course be bought in that way. For example it is common practice for a conveyor estimator to produce an estimate for the cost of a conveyor on a price per metre basis, applying factors for width, lift, power, etc. It is also common practice for the contract engineers (once the tender has been converted into an order) to purchase motors, gearboxes, belting and steelwork in packages, for subsequent building up into conveyors, either in the contractor's works or on site. Unless the estimate is 'converted' to the same format as the intended purchase format, there is no hope of either static or dynamic control.

It is therefore important that time is devoted (after the celebratory contract award festivities) to converting the estimate into a control document.

The control document

This will exist at several levels of detail. For senior management, the following breakdown would be sufficiently detailed:

- cost of materials (money)
- engineering (man-hours and money)
- project management (man-hours and money)
- installation (man-hours and money)
- commissioning (man-hours and money)
- contingency (money).

It should be noted that profit is not included as an element on the control document. It must obviously be reported with the same regularity as the control document is produced, but it should be reported in a contract profit report (usually covering several contracts), and not on a cost control document.

For the hands-on managers (i.e. project manager, project engineers, heads of specialist departments, etc.) each of the above elements will need to be broken down into manageable elements. For example, the materials element might be further broken down into either sections of the plant (e.g. coal handling plant, ash handling plant, boiler installation, turbo-alternator) or into purchase packages within those sections (e.g. coal plant electric motors, coal plant steelwork). The choice as to whether to include the additional level of reporting depends on the size of the project, and the numbers of intermediate levels of management.

101

In a similar way, the engineering estimate (which, as indicated above, should always be stated in man-hours as well as money terms) will be sub-divided into mechanical, civil, electrical, etc. This ensures that heads of those departments can be held accountable by the project manager for their performances against estimate.

Cost reporting

Having gone to the trouble of producing a control document in a form against which historical reporting, forecasting of outstanding costs, and variance analysis are possible, it is essential that the actual commitments and cost are correctly reported.

Many accountants have a tendency to want to report costs only when money changes hands, or to be more accurate, when a demand for money to change hands is made, i.e. receipt of an invoice. This is far too late for any possible corrective action to be taken, and indeed it gives a false picture of the status of contracts.

Commitment reporting could be an alternative heading for this section since it is the reporting of commitments to spend money (i.e. order placement) that is vital for proper dynamic control. This means that great care must be exercised over the paperwork associated with the placement or orders. It goes without saying that no order should be placed unless the following actions have been completed:

- A proper enquiry document, with engineering specification and conditions of contract, has been issued to suppliers.
- At least three quotations have been received, a tender comparison has been undertaken, and adjustments made to tenders where omissions/alterations to the required scope have been made.
- The project manager (and his superior in certain circumstances) has approved placing of the order, or has instituted actions to re-enquire/redesign if the lowest acceptable price significantly exceeds the estimate.

By this means, the managers of the contract have the opportunity to take action in time to prevent overspending, although it may not always be possible to achieve the desired results.

102

Forecasting

Accurate forecasting of costs still to be incurred is of paramount importance in the financial control of a contract. The original forecast of costs is the first estimate. As the contract progresses, these original forecasts turn into 'actuals' (commitment being the same as actual for contract control purposes). There will invariably be differences between the original forecast and actual — called variances — and these variances will add up to an overall variance on the contract to date. However, they are only part of the picture. The remaining expenditure is still to happen, and there will be the effects of further variances to be taken into account.

For activities that have not yet started, and are some time in the future such as installation and commissioning, it is unlikely that another estimate every month will be justified. Unless new information arrives, (e.g. a firm quotation from an installation contractor, or a large change in the scope of the work), it is likely that the initial estimate for activities not yet started will remain unchanged.

Some skill and judgement is required in forecasting costs still to come on activities already started. This applies particularly to activities with potential open-ended costs, (e.g. engineering and site work), and the fact of its difficulty is well-proven by the frighteningly large percentage of contracts that overrun their budgeted engineering and construction man-hours.

It is essential to ensure that proper attention is paid to man-hour monitoring, particularly in drawing offices. The best person to ask about the number of hours still required to complete a drawing is the draughtsman doing it. If the individual's answer seems to be unacceptable, he should be asked to justify it. His boss's comments will of course be invited, but the views of the person doing a task should not be ignored.

The paperwork

The essential requirements of a cost control system are that it is:

- easy to understand
- fast and easy to produce
- different degrees of detail for different levels of management are shown
- presentation can be graphical as well as tabular.

Reliable facts and dependable forecasts
The elements of the system are:

- the original estimate (i.e. *the budget*)
- approved variations to the original estimate
- the current approved estimate
- a commitment to date (perhaps also the commitment for the current month if the managers feel it helps)
- a forecast of costs still to be incurred
- an estimated final cost of the contract
- a forecast variance at the end of the contract

Each department, and each level of control management, requires a regular report (usually monthly) in which all of these elements have been updated and compared.

'Manpower' departments
Estimates and commitments for these departments should be based on expenditure of both man-hours and money. It is usual to record and forecast man-hours and costs on the same document. Fig. 5.1 is a typical engineering department summary document, where each discipline is recorded on a single line. Except for quite small projects, it is likely that each discipline will require a build-up sheet, where the engineering and draughting elements are treated separately. Indeed, as indicated earlier in the case of Drawing Office control, there is no short cut. The 'product' of a drawing office is a certain number of drawings; packages of drawings, or even individual drawings, need to be treated as items to be controlled. A similar document would be used for site labour cost control.

Purchasing control
The same type of document is used for the control of expenditure on materials and equipment. For uniformity, it is quite common to use an identical format, and merely leave the man-hours columns blank.

Total contract summary
This document forms the basis of the monthly report sent to the senior management (e.g. the Director of Projects). It records on one page the actual expenditure to date, forecast to comple-

Cost element	Original allowance		Variations to allowance		Current allowance		Committed to date		Required to complete		Total forecast cost at completion		Variance		Variance shown last month		Comments
	1		2		3(= 1 + 2)		4		5		6(= 4 + 5)		7(= 3 − 6)				
	Man-hours	Cost	Man-hours	Cost	Man-hours	Cost	Man-hours	Cost	Man-hours	Cost	Man-hours	Cost	Man-hours	Cost	Man-hours	Cost	
Mechanical engineering																	
Electrical engineering																	
Civil engineering																	
Instrumentation																	
etc																	

Fig. 5.1. Engineering department cost control summary document

105

Cost element	Original allowance 1		Variations to allowance 2		Current allowance 3(= 1 + 2)		Committed to date 4		Required to complete 5		Total forecast cost at completion 6(= 4 + 5)		Variance 7(= 3 − 6)		Variance shown last month		Comments
	Man-hours	Cost	Man-hours	Cost	Man-hours	Cost	Man-hours	Cost	Man-hours	Cost	Man-hours	Cost	Man-hours	Cost	Man-hours	Cost	
Engineering																	
Materials																	
Construction																	
Commissioning																	
Total																	

Fig. 5.2. Total contract cost control summary document

tion, and anticipated variances for each spending department involved in a contract. Fig. 5.2 is an example of the format.

A 'refined' alternative

This chapter deals with financial control, and in theory should not be concerned with physical control. However, as most readers will appreciate, the two impinge on each other, and should not be managed separately. Elements of physical control (e.g. redesign, lateness, materials not to specification) have a considerable bearing on the actual and/or forecast costs of a project.

A method of financial control that finds favour in many contracting companies is based on this interdependence, principally by recognizing that the cost of an activity or piece of equipment is merely one element of that activity. Others include duration and number of people involved.

This method is known as *PERT/cost*. This requires the estimated cost elements of an activity or piece of equipment to be assigned to that activity on a *PERT* network. Fig. 5.3 is a simplified example.

Control is quite simple, in that the planning engineer updates not only progress for the computer run, but also costs committed. Thus, if the 'time now' line in Fig. 5.3 is considered, it can be seen that the planning engineer has marked all activities to the left of the line with the actual resources used, i.e. numbers of people, durations and costs. Assuming that all of the activities to the left of the 'time now' line are completed at the time of assessment, and concentrating only on costs, the following can be calculated:

estimated cost at this point	£950
actual cost at this point	£1050

If there is no reason to alter the estimate for the final activity, the anticipated final cost will be £1560, compared with an original estimate of £1450.

Computerization

Whether the *PERT/cost* or the tabular method of reporting is used, much of the routine work can now be done quickly by using a computer.

It is quite common to combine physical progress reporting with financial reporting in a simple graph of expenditure (both forecast

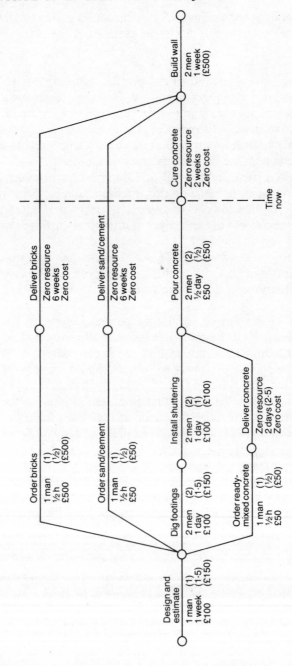

Fig. 5.3. PERT/cost network (figures in brackets represent actual amount of resources used)

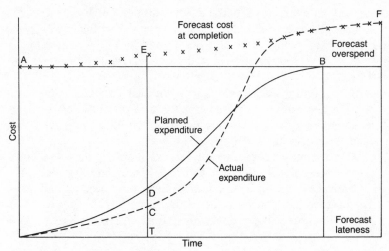

Fig. 5.4. Expenditure S-curve

and actual) against time. Because of its shape, this graph is referred to in the industry as an S-curve. Fig. 5.4 indicates how progress and cost can be effectively combined together in one presentation.

The solid curve represents the planned expenditure on a cumulative basis, and the solid horizontal line AB indicates what the estimated total cost is when the estimate is prepared.

The dotted curve represents the actual cumulative expenditure, and the crosses that form the line AEF are the regular estimates (usually monthly) of the total cost at completion.

The graph highlights requirements for action quickly. At time T, it can be seen that the actual expenditure C is lower than the forecast expenditure D, but the forecast of expenditure still to be made (E – C) is increased. At the 'time now' line ET (at this point nothing would exist to the right of the line) the project manager can be told the following:

- expenditure is lower than forecast
- forecast total project expenditure is higher than budget.

From this, the obvious deductions are that the project is running late (money is not being spent quickly enough) and the project is going to overrun its budget (what money has been spent has not bought what it should have). If no action is taken to correct matters, the picture will continue to be filled in as shown to the right of ET, and the project will have overrun both budget and time.

Although in practice nothing exists to the right of the 'time now' line ET, the complete revised graph can be produced by the computer, making the assumption that all activities not yet started will have their original durations and costs.

Once a contract begins to run late it is likely to get worse until corrective action is effective, and in any case lateness inevitably increases costs. A projected S-curve indicating overrun and over-expenditure is a concentrator of the mind which usually elicits immediate corrective action from the project manager.

Importance of reliable data

Whichever method of project cost control is used, its effectiveness is considerably reduced if the data used in its preparation are unreliable. Indeed, it can become dangerous to base decisions upon a cost control document with flawed data. Both factual (i.e. historic) data and forecast data must be reliable, and the expenditure of time and effort in ensuring the system produces reliable data is never wasted.

Historical data collection and recording should not be difficult. Material purchase commitments are invariably stated on the relevant purchase orders; sub-contracts are also normally documented. The main scope for error lies in recording man-hours.

This error can result from mere laziness (i.e. not correctly filling in a time sheet because of the effort involved in remembering) or from deviousness (deliberately mis-recording hours on a particular contract because it assists in hiding a current over-spend problem). The only weapon to combat both of these is constant vigilance and suspicion by several levels of management. For this to work effectively, the whole philosophy of the company must be geared toward knowing and understanding the importance of correct cost recording.

Forecast data, by its very nature, is usually wrong. The trick is to get it nearly right, and to improve estimating techniques. Not everybody can be good at estimating, and certainly no one person can be good at estimating everything. It is best to rely on the

110

individual responsible for a particular element of the contract (e.g. a draughtsman, or a chargehand fitter) to make the initial estimate, and then subject that — and the individual who made it — to close scrutiny.

Causes of variances

There are three broad categories of variance:

- design and estimating variances
- unforeseen costs
- underspending or overspending.

It is important to be able to differentiate between them in order that the financial responsibilties for correcting the variances may be properly apportioned.

Design and estimating variances. These are more often than not the responsibility of the contractor and the opportunity for obtaining recompense from the client to cover these variances is usually extremely limited.

The contractor will naturally learn from successive contracts that have suffered from design and estimating variances if something is amiss in design and estimating. This should be corrected, either by changes of personnel, training or the introduction of design and estimating procedures that give less latitude for individual error.

This type of variance almost invariably results in a profit erosion, although very occasionally in profit enhancement.

Unforeseen costs. These are the costs of carrying out work not envisaged when the tender was prepared. They may or may not be recoverable from the client depending on how well the original tender specified the scope of work that was included in the tender price.

Quite often arguments develop between the contractor and the client as to whether or not certain levels of non-destructive testing or quality assurance have or have not been included in the tender price. The only solution for the contractor is to fully specify what types of ancillary service work such as these are covered in his quotation.

However, even apart from the two examples cited above, the contractor is quite likely to encounter areas of work unforeseen when preparing the tender for which he will undoubtedly have

111

to carry the additional costs. Whether or not these unforeseen costs are recoverable from the client, it is imperative that the contractor's project manager ensures that proper records of them are maintained in order that, at the very least, future tenders take due recognition of the potential problems.

Underspending/overspending. These variances arise simply from an operation costing more than was estimated (or less than was estimated), and are a function solely of the quality of the original estimated prices used in the tender price build up.

Some contractors have such streamlined systems for estimating costs, and for updating these costs on a regular basis, that there is very little scope in the subsequent contract execution for over or under spending. Other contractors with somewhat less sophisticated systems rely upon the swings and roundabouts maxim to keep them out of total trouble.

This type of variance is always reflected in the eventual profit on the contract.

Variances and profit erosion or enhancement

Although profit reporting should not be allowed to confuse the analysis and recording of costs, there is a strong case to be made for including it in graphical form such as that shown in Fig. 5.5, where the effect of variations to the contract and forecast cost overruns can be seen.

This type of presentation should be reserved only for very senior management, who will need to make their own assessments of company profits, using individual contract profit trends as building blocks.

Dynamic control

The dynamic aspect of financial control is illustrated by considering some ways in which action can avoid or reduce profit erosion.

When a contractor is awarded a multi-million pound contract spread over a period of years, it represents a significant proportion of his financial and engineering capacity for some time to come.

The risk is high, both in terms of the loss which could arise on that particular contract and in terms of future business. It has to be made successful. In terms of value it could be equivalent to the turnover of a medium-sized engineering company of 2000

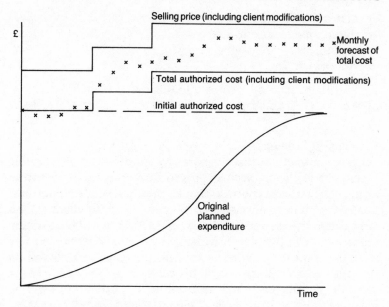

Fig. 5.5. Reporting of cost and profit

employees which would be managed by a board and highly-paid executives. The contract deserves no less a treatment. From its inception it should get the same expert attention in all its aspects as would the business undertaking of equivalent size. Any tendency to regard the contract as one of many should be vigorously resisted. From the initial enquiry stage the contract manager designate should be vested with the authority and the responsibility for ensuring its success.

Ideally, the engineer who was responsible for decisions during the tendering stage should become the contract manager when the order is received to ensure that all the factors and estimates built into the tender are carried into practical effect — a factor which has considerable impact upon subsequent financial control.

There are numerous channels through which the costs in a contract can be increased by bad contract management, such as:

- effects of the conditions of contract
- lateness
- finance costs

113

- increased material and labour costs
- purchasing arrangements
- insurances
- sub-contracting.

Each of them should be studied to determine their full financial implications. As an illustration, the first four are considered here.

Conditions of contract

Large contracts are usually placed by powerful and near or fully monopolistic clients, such as government agencies or industrial giants. The terms of contract, though possibly based on published model conditions, normally differ from client to client.[2] To a large extent this is sound common sense. A client will be investing much money in the project without the means of recovering any until the plant is operational, and will therefore seek conditions that enforce discipline upon all his contractors. At the tendering stage the contractor is in a relatively weak position. He will be in competition with others, and will not want his tender to appear less attractive than theirs by insisting upon a relaxation of the conditions. He may also feel that if ever he had to invoke his legal rights under the contract he could win his case but jeopardize his future business. He may therefore be content at the tendering stage to have the client's conditions vetted from the legal rather than the commercial standpoint.

This is understandable and may even be the correct course of action in most circumstances. However, once the contract is signed both parties are equally bound by its terms. The contractor should from that point on be as rigorous in enforcing them as is the client.

First, therefore, he must be quite clear as to what he has contracted to sell. If he has sold a Ford he should not provide a Rolls-Royce. He should ensure that only one individual, the project manager, has authority to vary the contract as sold, and that he is fully aware of the financial consequence of all modifications and concessions. It is true that the financial effect of such modification will be highlighted by the accounting procedures just dealt with, but the objective here is to take action necessary to avoid such variations arising.

Many modifications will be sought for the purpose of providing a better engineering product. The contractor is in business to survive, not to advance technology gratuitiously. No improvement should be supplied without recompense. The contractor must continually remind himself of the risk he is carrying. Success or failure on a large contract will affect his profits for years to come. He will have tied up so large a proportion of his capacity that the opportunity to spread his risks will be greatly reduced. He should not therefore feel discomforted if the client points out an improvement he could make in the design. He should counter this with a contractual modification-to-order form, requiring the client to pay the cost.

In many cases the client will have covered this point in the contract conditions. These may provide that the contractor is to carry out such additional work, up to 15% of the contract price, as instructed in writing by the client, such work to be at a price to be mutually agreed between the parties.[3] This is not unreasonable. Because the client is investing heavily in the project he will not want work delayed to agree the cost of a relatively small extra. However, there is a danger when a commercial officer in the client's employ queries the extra prior to accepting it. He will rightly ask such questions as 'Wasn't it already included? Didn't the contractor derive some benefit from the work? Wouldn't he have had to do it later in any case? Hasn't he got a claim on his insurers?" The longer the discussion continues, the greater the number of such extras, and the less chance the contractor has of receiving an order for the extra.

This is a recurrently difficult situation, but it can be met in part. If the main purpose of the condition is to prevent discussion on a small extra from delaying the contract, the client may be prepared to place a firm order within certain limits. An attempt should always be made therefore to include in the contract terms authority for the client's and the contractor's resident engineers to bind their employers by any agreements on extras up to a certain value. Such a clause by its nature will always favour the client, but as the contractor will by this means be assured of getting a firm order for say £10 000 he may prefer it to arguing about the actual cost of £12 500 some years later with the chance of getting far less.

When additional work is beyond the scope of such an arrangement, it is imperative for the contractor not to incur the extra cost unless the instruction is in writing, and that immediately afterwards a quotation is submitted. The client must then be urged

115

continuously until he agrees the value, for as time passes and the number of extras grows, the contractor gradually loses the initiative and may find himself agreeing a single amount to cover all extras at the end of the contract.

Notwithstanding the difficulties of agreement concerning values, the contractor must always press upon the client the effect that extras will have upon delivery. If he fails to obtain extensions to the completion date, he will find himself at risk over penalties and increased costs arising after the contractual completion date.

The terms of contract govern both parties, and the contractor should use them to his advantage whenever possible. It is rare indeed that the client has no part to play in the completion of the contract. Any delays on the client's part or any non-compliance should be brought to his notice immediately with a request for any necessary extension of time and/or an increase in price. This is not vindictive. Whenever there is such a mutual jogging in the early stages of a project it normally gets off to a very good start. Others take longer before they start to move. In addition, it is always prudent to have documentary evidence in the form of claims, minutes of site meetings and photographs of the difficulties created by others but borne by the contractor whenever bargaining may be required.

Lateness

Experience shows that any contract which is running late is also running into a loss. It may be that the factors that cause the lateness are also themselves sources of loss, for example, faulty welding discovered at test. But apart from this, time itself costs money. Increased costs are higher at the tail end of a contract. Material delivered out of turn requires uneconomical use of labour and equipment. Late delivery of material may cause the redeployment of men and equipment then engaged on other phases. Penalties may be incurred, import licences may expire, force majeure clauses may be vitiated, payment of accounts delayed, retention monies withheld, and the next contract due for execution placed in jeopardy. Time is money, and all personnel should be trained to understand this.

The design engineer who puts forward an improvement during the course of the contract, with supporting evidence to show that it actually reduces costs, should always be asked to include the cost of time in his calculations.

In order to safeguard the programme, the following steps must be taken. In the first place, there must exist a contract programme in sufficient detail to be monitored, following the same principles which earlier were shown to be a necessary element in the monitoring of cost. The only difference is that here a time allowance is being dealt with. Systems for monitoring and controlling programmes are available in a variety of forms, and the good project manager will insist on strict adherence to the programme — as rigorously as he insists on adherence to the budget.

It is difficult to see how the financial effect of lateness can be effectively controlled unless a project manager is appointed over the entire contract work, covering the design office, the works, and the site. He must have authority to make judgements and take decisions apparently costly in themselves, but effectively cost-cutting in terms of time. For example, Sunday and holiday working is relatively expensive and may not be envisaged in the contract. If it is necessary to keep the contract up to schedule, the decision should be taken by the project manager for that reason alone, even though it is apparently adding to the costs.

No manufacture goes through just by the force of paperwork. Every operation must be expedited. This is particularly true of outside suppliers. The customer who expedites most strenuously gets his goods the soonest; the customer who never expedites is last in the queue. To prevent a supplier or sub-contractor causing a delay he must be expedited strenuously and regularly.

The result of lateness may be completely disproportionate to the value of the late material. The commissioning of an entire installation, for example, may be delayed by the late delivery of one valve. Control of such suppliers is therefore vital, but to be effective it must be done by the right people in the right manner. If it is carried out by a progress chaser who regards his job as the recording of continually revised programme dates and the passing on of fresh delivery promises, it is bound to fail. It must be carried out by those who are aware of the financial implications and with the power to impose penalties.

Some companies find that the most suitable persons are the company's buyers, the very people from whom the supplier expects to get further orders. Just as the contractor is anxious not to lose the custom of the main purchaser, so the supplier is anxious not to lose the custom of the contractor. The contractor is therefore in a position to use to his own advantage the forces that are being brought to bear on him. If he uses these forces intelligently he will be able to help the supplier to maintain delivery dates, not only by the economic pressure he can bring to bear, but also by his ability to arrange further sub-contracting and purchasing to assist the supplier in difficulties.

Finance costs

The cost of finance is often a shock to engineers. A contract spread over six years, with terms of payment allowing 80% against delivery of individual shipments, 15% on completion and 5% on taking over 12 months thereafter, will incur financing costs amounting to 8 or 9% of the contract price.

It is doubtful if the contractor would be allowed to add the full cost of financing to the tender price because the client would argue that much of the financing came from share capital and reserves, which is rewarded by profit, not interest, and is therefore not strictly a cost. It is therefore necessary for the contractor to keep his financing costs down, and incidentally also the capital costs of the equipment, by negotiating the most favourable terms of payment from the client.

One of the disadvantages of the conventional method of payment against shipment is the difficulty of assessing the value of shipments. Usually, an estimated cost per tonne is used as the calculating factor, and for one reason or another this often results in the final shipment having an absurdly inappropriate value compared with the cost of the work. The solution is to agree with the client for payment to be made against time or work done and for the tender price to reflect such financing of work-in-progress.

The means by which this is best done (from the contractor's viewpoint) is the planned payment chart. This chart is nothing more than the contract programme agreed with the client expressed in terms of money and it is set out in Table 5.1.

The contract envisaged is a simple one of only two main items, each item being broken down into the elements of design, manufacture, supply, construction, commissioning and miscellaneous services. Each of these factors is the subject of a line on the contract programme with commencement and completion dates. It

118

Table 5.1. Expenditure/planned payment

Item	Expenditure	1	2	3	13	14	15	16	17	18	19	20	21	22	23	24	Total
A	Design and engineer	1	1	1													4
	Manufacturing				5	3	1										40
	Outside supply				2	2	2	2	2	2	2	1	1	1	1		16
	Construction																16
	Commissioning														1		5
	Miscellaneous services															1	2
B	Design and engineer		1														2
	Manufacturing					1	4	6	2	2	2	2	1				30
	Outside supply					4	4	2	2	2	2	2	1	1	1	1	30
	Construction						2										14
	Commissioning											2	1				4
	Miscellaneous services														1		1
Totals	Design and engineer	1	1	1													6
	Manufacturing				4	4	2	6	2	4	4	2	2				70
	Outside supply				4	2	4	4	2	4		1	2	2	2		46
	Construction						4	4	4								30
	Commissioning										1	2	1				9
	Miscellaneous services															1	3
	Total monthly expenditure	1	1	1	2	2	119	10	6	4	5	3	4	2	2	2	164
	Total cumulative expenditure	1	2	3	5	7	126	136	142	146	151	154	158	160	162	164	164
	Cumulative percentage expenditure/contract payments	0.6	1.2	1.8	3.0	4.3	76.8	82.9	86.6	89.0	92.1	93.9	96.3	97.6	98.8	100	100

Contract month

119

is a relatively simple matter to place the appropriate portion of the contract value against each and thus produce a chart showing when it is anticipated that the contract payments will fall due. Assuming that the contract programme is maintained, both parties are aware of the cash commitment at any given time. Payment of accounts then follows the approval by the client of the contractor's progress statements. The advantages to both parties are obvious. The contractor has no complicated calculations to do apart from an initial compilation of the planned payment chart. His work-in-progress is financed, and he can budget his cash requirements relatively accurately. The client is provided with a powerful influence on the contractor's progress: if the work is late, so is payment. The planned payment chart can be used similarly with suppliers and sub-contractors to bring to bear upon them exactly the same disciplines being borne by the contractor.[4]

Some clients will not agree to use planned payment charts but can usually be persuaded to pay against 'contract milestones'. These milestones are completion of significant events in the contract programme (e.g. completion of drawings and delivery of material to fabricators) about which little if any doubt can exist that they have actually happened. An undertaking to pay agreed sums of money when these milestones have been achieved leaves little scope for dispute, and ensures a cash flow in line with expectations — provided the programme is maintained.

In the absence of a phased payment schedule or a milestone payment schedule, it is up to the contractor to ensure that he does not add to his financing costs by being late with his invoices or by failing to follow them up to get paid. It is always advisable to arrange a close liaison between the project manager and the accountant in charge of claims, so that the accountant is aware of the physical state of the contract before demanding payment, and the project manager is aware of late payments when he sits down with the customer to discuss progress. In any case it is preferable to discuss differences regarding accounts in person. Apart from the clearer understanding obtained, it is cheaper. If sending a man a hundred or so miles once or twice a month ensures the prompt payment of accounts, it is worth the expense, for an account of £100 000 costs between £30 and £40 for each day it is outstanding.

It is equally important to apply rigorous cash control to suppliers and sub-contractors. Wherever possible, without jeopardising

120

the price, payment terms must be negotiated with suppliers that minimize the amount of cash outstanding between payment of the supplier and receipt of payment from the client.

Increased material and labour costs

Under modern conditions it appears inevitable that material prices and labour wages will escalate, i.e. rise during a contract because of inflation. Many model conditions of contract therefore include clauses for contract price adjustment (CPA) to compensate for those changes of cost that are beyond contractors' control, although with the lower inflation costs of the mid-1980s, and following government pressure on nationalised industries to reduce capital expenditure, many contracts are nowadays being placed on fixed prices.[5]

Where CPA is allowed for in a contract, contractors who are members of a trade association use the formula agreed by the association within that particular industry. It is doubtful whether such formulae have any real relevance to the type of contract that is being discussed. Their weakness lies in their use of average situations, such as mid-way dates and straight-line incidence. These are adequate for smaller contracts which do not justify the use of *PERT*/cost techniques or planned payment charts, but in the type of contract being considered their presence is anachronistic, though still widespread.

Every contractor before tendering should consider if the adjustment proposed in the client's conditions of contract is adequate. The relative influence of direct and indirect factors affecting costs can change quickly and such formulae need frequent revision. For example, consider a formula which, when compiled a few years ago, included only two elements, manufacturing labour and materials, in the ratio of 60:40. As the cost of labour historically increases at a faster rate than materials, in the intervening years labour may well have risen by 50% while materials may have risen by only 25%. Today, therefore, the ratio should stand at 90:50 or 64:36, but unless the formula is revised, contractors would still be being reimbursed for changes on the now inadequate basis of 60:40. Alternatively, the formula may have been based upon factors which are no longer applicable, such as the size or numbers of units, type or mix of labour, location, types of material, or performance requirements.

If the formula is out of date or if its elements are not wholly applicable to a particular contractor or to a particular contract, a contractor may lose a great deal of money. Increased costs on a contract lasting six years (a not uncommon length of contract in the power industry) are likely to amount to between 25% and 50% of the contract price. Only a small amount of processing is needed to devise a better formula, as all price adjustment formulae are based on three factors: proportion, incidence and indices. These are related to the required number of elements, e.g. manufacturing labour, construction labour and materials.

To compile a formula or to check the feasibility of his association's formula a contractor first needs to know the proportion of the contract price that each element bears, and then a series of indices against which he can monitor the rises in costs. On the materials side he will no doubt find a government index or a combination of indices which approximate to the material content of his contract. On the labour side he will need to compile his own, based on his own mix of skills and labour categories. This is a fairly intricate job initially, but having been compiled the monitoring of the index is simple. The contractor now has all the ingredients of a custom-built increased cost formula.

As the contract progresses the contractor knows his monthly expenditure in the areas of manufacturing and construction labour and material. He adjusts these costs by the percentage increase or decrease in the indices since the price basis date, and then computes within fairly close limits of accuracy his increased costs. A comparison with the amount which he is recovering from the formula enables both the customer and the contractor to assess the adequacy of the formula governing the contract, and puts the contractor in a position to press for a change in the formula within his industry. Even if he cannot change the industry's formula, his formula is still important for his own assessment of profit erosion. The process of collecting *actual* increased costs is a practical impossibility, and if an inadequate recovery of increased costs is one source of erosion, the contractor needs to have a domestic formula by which to compute the likely under-recovery.

Standard formulae are not applicable to large-scale contracts, and it would be better for the client and the contractor to agree increased cost payments on the basis of actual rather than notional conditions. For prototype contracts especially, where no history of proportions, incidence or indices exists, it would be unwise for either of them to use an existing formula, and in such a case the only realistic solution is to compile a formula for that contract alone.

At the tender stage a contractor should therefore satisfy himself that the formula proposed in the client's contract documents is adequate protection against these potential increased costs. If he finds that the proposed contract formula is inadequate, it is obviously incumbent upon him to draw that to the attention of the client, and if at all possible to arrange its replacement by one that will give protection. There is no reason why the contractor should not propose a formula devised by himself, but this does run the risk of inviting stern opposition from the client, and an insistence that the contractor quotes in accordance with the already prepared contract conditions. A far better approach, and one that is gaining more and more favour in the contracting industry of late, is for the trade association to adopt a more forceful role with clients and client organizations in negotiating sensible CPA formulae that will apply throughout the industry.

Summary
Financial control demands little more than disciplined budgeting and common sense. At the tender stage all cost elements must be identified and programmed. Each company division must be given its appropriate cost allowance, and be made responsible for taking action to minimize variances. Variances will occur (both positive and negative) but the project manager must ensure that they are not accepted merely as part of a reporting procedure.

On the practical side, the project managers, engineers, buyers, workpeople, and staff must be trained to think in terms of money, and to assess every action and every inaction in terms of its effect upon the profitability of the contract. The real financial control of the project is vested in them, not in the accountants.

Notes
1. By 'variance' here is meant any change causing variations from the basis for first estimating the cost of a contract, not the particular meaning of variance used in statistical theory.
2. For instance, see the model form of general conditions of contract MF/1 published in 1988 by the Institution of Mechanical Engineers, the Institution of Electrical Engineers and the Association of Consulting Engineers.

3. For instance, clause 27 in the above model conditions of contract states the contractor's obligations to act on instructions to vary the work, but within limits.
4. In many conditions of contract a contractor is required to place sub-contracts with corresponding obligations on payments, variations, etc.
5. The abbreviation CPA should be used with care, as it can denote critical path analysis or contract price adjustment. There are alternative phrases for the latter, such as prime cost adjustment, the language varying from industry to industry.

Further reading

Horgan, M.O. and Roulston, F.R. *Project control of engineering contracts*. Spon, London, 1988.

Johnston, K.F.A. *Electrical and mechanical engineering contracts*. Gower Press, Aldershot, 1971.

Ludwig, E.E. *Applied project management for the process industries*, 3rd edn. Gulf Publishing, Houston, 1977.

Lock, D. (ed.) *Handbook of engineering management*, chap. 20. Heinemann, London, 1988.

Marsh, P.D.V. *Contracting for engineering and construction projects*, 2nd edn. Gower Press, Aldershot, 1981.

6 Financial control of construction

'It is a truth very certain that, when it is not in our power to determine what is true, we ought to follow what is most probable' — *Descartes*.

Despite his experience of military life the philosopher Descartes presumably did not have the financial control of construction in mind; but his thought is appropriate. No one can say with certainty what a new power station or a new bus shelter will cost, yet there usually has to be financial control from the start of their design and construction. The techniques for this control are based on probabilities. In this chapter application of the principles of control in the conditions of uncertainty and risk characteristic of construction and related industries is discussed.

The authors of this book are united in two beliefs. One is that the methods of control of a project should be appropriate not only to its objectives and size, but also to the uncertainties inherent in predicting its cost, timing and the risks of changes. Some uncertainties are common to all types of project, although of different magnitude. The probabilities of promoters changing their minds, of productivity forecasts being wrong, of interest rates changing, and of labour disputes occurring are measures of uncertainty in this class. Construction financial control uncertainties include these and others which are more characteristic of it, such as uncertain ground conditions, weather influences, selection of the contractor and a generally high level of uncertainty in predicting the performance of plant and people.

The second belief is that control must include action. Many cost control schemes are no more than cost recording procedures because

125

they stop short of actually initiating corrective action. The important consideration here is that the action must be corrective. Arbitrarily chosen action will seldom be corrective. To select between alternative actions requires that the consequences of each must be forecast. Since consequences cannot be forecast with certain truth, action must be selected by comparison of the most probable consequences.

Financial control comprises the prediction of the cost effects of technical decisions. Technical decisions in this sense cover all the decisions to be taken in the cycle of engineering project activity. They include design, selection of contract procedures and contractors, estimating, cost control, resolution of unexpected problems and settlement of accounts. Decisions affecting a balance between operating and construction costs can be seen in the same way.

Probabilities

All financial control processes involve prediction in monetary terms, and so it must be appreciated that all such predictions have an element of uncertainty. If an estimate is prepared for a part of a project, there is a probability that it will be correct to within a percentage of the actual cost. There is a probability distribution which shows how the actual cost may be expected to differ from estimated or predicted cost. Financial control predictions do not have a mathematically pure distribution of probable error, but the error distribution character of many predictions can be observed. Examples are given when referring to particular techniques in this chapter.

Timing

The effectiveness of a cost control decision is vitally affected by timing. This arises in three ways, as follows:

- A decision taken too early may turn out to have been wrong when more data are later available. For example, a design decision made too early may unnecessarily constrict alternatives for subsequent decisions so that the optimum complete design is never considered. Late decisions are equally untimely because they lead to more costly site work than is necessary. This is because economy in construction requires flexibility for application of resources, otherwise they may be under-used. Late decisions constrict alternatives for construction work itself in the same way as early decisions constrict design. To take a simple example — cancellation of work immediately before it was to be done would save much less labour cost than if the contractor was able to adjust his plan well in advance.

- Control decisions have to take account of the origins of construction costs. These depend on timing in a way which classical cost control generally ignores. Now that most site activity comprises the assembly of plant and labour teams whose content is inflexible and whose economic range of output is therefore narrow, more of the total cost of work is proportional to the time that such teams are employed and less to the quantities of work they produce. Consequently, planning and co-ordination of activity influence the cost of work much more than formerly. Systems of predictive financial control must take this into account.

- Control requires prediction of the *timing* of the payments and receipts as well as their *amounts*. Higher interest rates on money, and greater client concern with controlling the return on invested capital require the project cash flows to be predicted and used as a facet of financial control.

Calculating viability

As described in chapter 2, discounted cash flow (DCF) techniques involve simple calculations of net present worth and DCF rate of return. Both are applications of the ordinary compound interest calculation taught at school.

The net present worth of a group of payments, to be made at various times in the future, is the minimum amount of money which the payer should have available now in order to be able to make all the future payments. It is assumed that until the last payment is made the balance not yet paid will earn interest at a particular rate. Whether the money is actually available at the start or not, the net present worth is an effective single figure measurement of the *cost* of a project which takes the timing of payments into account.

The DCF rate of return is a similar single figure measurement which represents the benefit of a group of payments received at various times in relation to a group of payments made. Its calculation is explained in Appendix 2.1. When a project involves both payments and receipts, their effect is from time to time to add to or reduce the amount of money currently invested in the project. This pattern of fluctuating investment over time is the cash flow. If the position at the end of the time scale is a profit, the profit can be expressed as a return on the investment made. The DCF rate of return is the product of one method of calculating this return. It is the hypothetical rate of interest which would need to be earned on investments and charged on loans to achieve the given cash flow, if the capital were to be invested instead of being used to carry out the project.

Clearly, if the predicted rate of return from a proposed project is less than prevailing bank interest rates, the project is not commercially viable. Although it might produce a 'profit' in the sense that income would exceed expenditure, the profit is less than that which would have been achieved by investment if the project had not been carried out at all. The internal rate of return is a powerful measurement of the *profitability* of a project which takes the timing of payments into account. It is usually calculated as a percentage per annum.

With no significant exceptions, present worth can be used with advantage in financial control of construction in place of cost, and DCF rate of return in place of per cent profit. This applies equally to promoter and contractor.

Predictions of net present worth and rate of return can often influence decisions and improve control. For example, a tender can be adjusted to increase return without increasing its amount, or a design which may be attractive on comparison of cost may not be the best on comparison of net present worth.

At this point, three important principles of construction financial control can be stated:

- Financial control is decisions influenced by monetary prediction.
- All prediction involves uncertainty, which should be taken into account and measured.
- Financial control decisions may be misguided if the influence of timing on the monetary prediction is ignored.

Some of the main tasks which make up construction financial control are now considered in the light of these principles.

Planning and feasibility studies

At this stage of a construction project, the most uncertain predictions of likely cost and timing are made. A range of accuracy of ± 33% will include most estimates for feasibility studies. The promoter's commitment to proceed should be based on such predictions. Contingency allowances should then be at their highest.

Contingency allowances

Contingency or risk allowances arise from the uncertainties of cost estimating. The engineer or designer is more likely to underestimate the number of cost generating influences than to overestimate them. This may be a general psychological tendency. It is also a practical reaction to the difficulty of foreseeing the extent of unexpected money-consuming problems which completing the project will have to face. It would require a science deeper even than psychology to explain the certain truth that unexpected events which cost money occur far more frequently than those which save it. The further from the completion of the project the cost or time predictions are being made, the harder such influences are to foresee. Contingency allowances are a means of compensating for this characteristic of project financial control. In the past they have usually be guessed or derived unsystematically from previous experience. If the incidence of uncertainty is recognized, it can be measured, and can allow contingency allowances to be used positively to improve control.

As a simplified example, assume that an early estimate of the cost of a project comprises separate estimates for the civil, structural and plant components of an industrial project, as shown in Table 6.1. Each component of the estimate has a probability of error. The estimate of the civil cost depends on assumptions about ground conditions and it is therefore probably more uncertain than the others. It is also more likely to be an underestimate than an overestimate. From records of previous experience, it is possible to estimate a likely percentage error either side of the cost estimate. It is helpful to think of these error percentages not as maximum possible errors, but as errors with a likely probability of occurrence. If, for example, the criterion used is a one in three probability of the stated error being exceeded, this is approximately equivalent to the standard deviation of the error probability distribution being the percentage error stated.

CONTROL OF ENGINEERING PROJECTS

Table 6.1.   Synthesis of a construction cost estimate

Cost element	Cost estimate	1 in 3 probable error	
		Low: %	High: %
Civil works	£2300 000	16	7
Structural works	£1850 000	11	8
Plant	£3210 000	7	6
Services	£1030 000	12	4
Total	£8390 000		

Using figures like those given in Table 6.1, an error distribution for the total estimate can be produced. It is produced by sampling a large number of possible combinations of the cost estimates for the parts of the project defined. The calculation is a standard computer routine. It is called the Monte Carlo method because of its similarity to the problem of assessing the odds on very complex gambles.

The error distribution is shown in Fig. 6.1. It indicates that the *most likely* total cost is greater than the total cost actually estimated. It also estimates the probability of any other cost being exceeded or not reached. Hence a graph of the type shown in Fig. 6.2 can

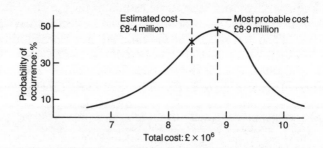

From an assessment of the ranges of possible error in the elements of a construction cost estimate, the stages of calculation illustrated enable contingency and risk allowances to be set to assist financial control for the promoter or contractor

Fig. 6.1.   Probability distribution of error in total estimate

130

be produced which shows the probability of excess cost if the target cost is set at different percentages above the currently estimated cost.

This is a very useful device for the designer to use in adding contingency allowances to cost estimates submitted to promoters. Only promoters can determine what probability of excess cost is tolerable within their limitations on acquisition of capital, or the return to be achieved on its investment. This probability defines the contingency to be allowed by reference to a graph such as that given in Fig. 6.2.

The same technique can be used by a contractor when submitting a tender. In this case the acceptable probability of making a low profit margin defines the 'risk' allowance to be made. Where timing is of special importance, the same technique can be used to judge the allowances which should be made to protect a target net present worth or rate of return.

This technique has been described in detail to show how recognition of the uncertainty in financial control can itself lead to better control. Uncertainty can be measured by assessment of

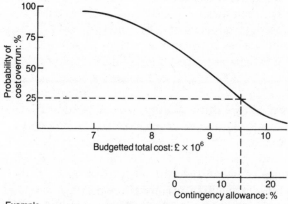

Example

If only a 1 in 4 (25%) probability of cost overrun is acceptable, budget for total cost of £9550 000, i.e. add contingency of 13·5% to current estimate.

Select acceptability of cost overrun from vertical axis. Read off percentage contingency allowance to be added to current cost estimate from lower horizontal axis.

Fig. 6.2. Curve for selection of contingency allowance

probable errors. The level of uncertainty about any prediction, whether of the nature, cost or timing of the work to be done, is a function of two things — the volume of decisions made relative to the total volume of decisions yet to be made, and the accuracy of the predictions on which these decisions are based.

There is another less clinical way in which contingency analysis can be used as a positive help to financial control. The project manager hoping to complete the work within a budget must ensure that the decision-makers in all the disciplines in his team are as foresighted as they can be in assessing the cost implications of their decisions. The earlier the stage in the project cycle at which they confront the reconciliation of the availability of money to their technical expectations for their sector of the work the better.

To this end, it has proved very effective for project managers to carve an inflated contingency allowance from the budget of projects right at the start and to release amounts from it to the decision-makers as the work progresses only after they have produced strenuously justified arguments for so doing. Not only does this tactic increase the likelihood of there still being enough money left in the contingency allowance for the later unexpected problems, it also forces the members of a project team to confront the issues affecting use of the available money within their sectors of the work much earlier than they ordinarily would. It has a third benefit in that it assures that adjustment of the proportion of the total amount of money available between the various competing sectors is a matter which remains in the control of the overall project manager.

Design

Financial control during design is comprised of predictions of the costs of the alternative designs which comply with the brief. This applies to all design decisions, from selection of type of structure down to selection of sizes of small components. It is usual to cost alternatives on the basis of the unit costs of the various components which will be required. Probabilities should be borne in mind at this stage so that the problem of selecting a prediction from varying historic unit costs can be confidently treated.

Increasingly, the likely construction method must be taken into account so that the influence it has on cost and timing are considered. The total cost of mechanized construction is not directly proportional to the quantities of components produced. Design

132

costing using unit costs for a tonne of steel or a cubic metre of concrete will not lead to control. This illustrates a general point about control of construction. Each contribution to the project activity, planning, design or construction, since it involves prediction, must be based on knowledge of what comes after; it is seldom important to know what went before. Design decisions are likely to be misguided if taken in ignorance of how the construction work is affected by them, but constrution work can proceed almost without sense of how the design was selected.

To illustrate the point, suppose that two alternative details for a concrete frame building involve the same volume of concrete and area of formwork. One may have clear slab soffits, the other a downstand at the perimeter of the slabs. In the first case table formwork could be used, in the second it could not. In this simple example it would be reasonable to expect the designer to be aware of the cost effect of his decision, but as a higher proportion of the cost of construction work becomes dependent on coordination and utilization of teams of plant and labour, the designer relying on unit cost records for his predictions of future cost will make more wrong decisions. The use of method-related charges in bills of quantities[1] or or priced activity schedules[2] as the financial control basis for contracts mitigate this problem by relating the prices paid to contractors more closely to their methods of construction.

Tendering and contracts

As most of the design decisions have been taken by this stage, the contingency has narrowed and the timing of the project become less uncertain. The importance of the selection of contract arrangements appropriate to financial control cannot be over-emphasized. It is not simply a matter of tying the contractor down to the most inflexible contract sum. When, for example, it is in the promoter's financial interest to enable technical improvements to be embodied in the project as construction proceeds, a financially flexible contract is essential. Similarly, there are situations where the promoter's financial interest is better served by the letting of contracts with a more precise time commitment than cost commitment.

So that the designer, superintending engineer or project manager can continue to influence the project to the promoter's advantage, it is important that the contract reflects the promoter's interest in the way the contractor carries out the project. Conventional conditions of contract tend to assume that minimum total cost is always the overriding control criterion. The importance to the promoter of predictability of timing of completion and of cash flows resulting from the contract tend to be under-emphasized.

Responsibility for control

The details of the contract made between promoter and contractor should derive from a clear understanding of the factors over which the promoter wishes to retain control, and those which he is intending should be left to the contractor.

It is conventional to think of alternative forms of contract as distributing risk in various ways. This can give a wrong impression, as also discussed in chapter 4. The risks to be considered are not confined to 'who takes responsibility if unexpected event A occurs', where A might be either fire, earthquake, or unforeseen ground conditions. These are only the low probability events; contracts have to predetermine responsibility for the consequences of all uncertainties, whether of low or high probability.

The likelihood of there being variations to the work itself, required by the promoter or designer, is an uncertainty for which the promoter normally takes responsibility. Responsibility in this sense means responsibility for any changed effort required from the contractor as a result of the variation. The changed effort will be measured in money and lead to adjustments of the payment to the contractor.

There is also uncertainty about the amount of effort which the contractor will have to apply to complete construction even if there are no variations. In a fixed price or measure and value contract, responsibility for this uncertainty lies with the contractor. If his costs vary from his predictions he must himself absorb their effect on his profit. In a cost reimbursement contract, the promoter does take responsibility for this type of uncertainty. These examples of responsibility for uncertainty may be self evident, but they illustrate a principle which can be applied to all the provisions of a contract except those which are purely administrative.

Alternative types of contract

Recognition of the function of contracts in these terms simplifies understanding of the alternatives available. How should responsibility for uncertainties be allocated? What considerations govern the choice?

Using the example of the cost reimbursement contract, this form only contributes to control when the promoter is best able to control the uncertainties of contractor effort, not the contractor himself. Clearly, this only happens when the work content is itself highly uncertain, and when for the contractor to assume this responsibility would require him to make such a massive allowance in his price for uncertainty that the promoter would lose control of the finances of the project. Control would have been lost in the sense that there would be little correlation between the amount of money paid to the contractor and the amount of effort expended by him. There would be a probability of the promoter securing a very cheap project, as there would of him having to pay far too much. Since these probabilities would be roughly equal, the promoter would be indulging in a game of chance, the opposite of maintaining financial control.

In choices between less extreme alternative contracts the same considerations apply. If, for example, a contract may include a cost escalation clause, it would be adopted only if the promoter considered the uncertainties of predicting cost escalation sufficient to justify assuming responsibility for them himself. There is no question of his 'saving' money by not having a cost escalation clause, he only suppresses his responsibility for the effects of uncertain cost escalation and asks the contractor to make an allowance for it instead. The question raised by analysing contracts in this way is that of deciding on whom the responsibility for accepting the various uncertainties should be laid. Some patterns of risk allocation are more conducive to control than others. Since economy stems from minimizing the effort absorbed in achieving a particular object, if the extent of that effort is uncertain, who is most likely to achieve effective control of it? Clearly, it is the party who has agreed to bear the consequences of ineffective control. The contract can, therefore, in placing responsibility, determine who will apply expertise to achieving economy in particular phases of the work.

To produce overall economy consequently requires that the work be allocated to those groups of people who are likely to be best at predicting their own types of uncertainty. Each separate source of uncertainty should be contractually allocated to the group who can best predict it.

In the normal competitive tender, the contractor is given the task of predicting the minimum effort required to complete a task, and then of doing the work within his prediction if he can. That remains the best contractual policy so long as the contractor really can predict the cost of the work with no greater uncertainty than characterizes the whole of the project control task. It is not, for example, making things too easy for the contractor to absolve him of responsibility for unforeseen ground conditions. It will actually save money for the promoter, except in the rare situation where the contractor has recently dug a big hole on the other side of the fence and knows exactly what he will find.

Target cost contracts, considered in this way, are only an attempt to preserve some contractor responsibility for *cost* uncertainty when the *work content* uncertainty is too high for the contractor to accept total responsibility. Promoters should appreciate that contractor responsibility is inevitably diluted when target cost contracts are used, and that consequently there is a lower probability of achieving the most economical result.

Contractors' estimating

This is the most obvious instance of control being a process of prediction. Many of the misunderstood aspects of the process stem from disregard of its probabilistic nature. For example, it is generally thought that contractors when submitting tenders vary their figures considerably, owing to market pressures, buying jobs, and other mysterious influences. In fact, the majority of the spread of tender prices is due to the probability distribution which is the measure of the accuracy with which the contractor is able to predict the cost of the work.

The spread of tenders

It has been shown that the characteristic error in building estimating is of the order of 7% standard deviation. This means that approximately two out of three cost estimates are within ±7% of the actual cost, and that about one in twenty are more than 15% in error.

To show how this affects tender lists, suppose that a group of contractors tendering for one job all added the same profit and risk allowance to their estimates of cost. With eight tenders submitted the average spread would be from a lowest tender of 100%

136

to a highest of 118%. Since tenderers make different predictions about methods of work, the actual spread is usually slightly wider than this.

Because tender prices appear unpredictable it is assumed that they are heavily adjusted after the net cost has been estimated. Once the uncertainties are recognized and measured, the influence of these adjustments is seen to be small.

The accuracy of contractor's estimating provides a baseline for consideration of the accuracy of cost prediction earlier in the project cycle. Contractor's estimators are specialists whose task is to predict the cost of construction work. They use information about the predicted work content which is more refined than at any earlier stage. Earlier predictions by less professional predictors must therefore be more uncertain. If contractors' estimators achieve a standard deviation of 5–10%, it is unlikely that prior estimating by designers will be better than 15–20% or by students of feasibility better than 20–30%.

Unit cost or operational estimating?

The techniques of contractor's estimating have advanced from the adherence to unit costs still characteristic of designer's estimating. Contractors increasingly recognize that predictions of cost are better compiled by consideration of the expected use of plant and labour on the project. It is now common for all the plant and labour costs to be assessed from a detailed prediction of the methods and programme of work.

Although dependent on the quantities of work, these costs are no longer proportional to them and cannot be so assessed. Selection of plant and labour teams and prediction of the time for which they will be required is directly in terms of the factors which are actually controlled on the site and is therefore more accurate. Materials and sub-contract costs remain proportional to quantities.

Site cost control

Site cost control serves overall construction financial control by leading to the economic use of plant, labour and materials on the site.

The type of cost control stemming from the quantity surveyor's 'cost plan' approach is suspect at this point. Its 'give and take' method of preserving total cost targets can lead to a confusing density of variations which make the use of resources unpredictable and wasteful. It generates claims which can destroy the contractor's control and dilute the promoter's by forcing payment into high uncertainty of amount and timing. Even if the extra costs incurred by the contractor are eventually compensated, the cash flow predictions on which he may have based his control will have been substantially upset.

Contractor's cost control usually consists of recording costs in order to prompt corrective action when there are 'variances'. This is quite different from the predictive basis of control. The variance is a variance from a budget, itself an earlier prediction of cost. There is no reason why current performance should be judged in relation to an earlier, and therefore cruder, prediction. If the primary object of control is economy, and earlier predictions have a higher measured probability of error, why adopt one of them as the target? Why should a contractor apply management effort to reducing the cost of a loss-making operation when another making a profit may be carried out at an unnecessarily high cost? Estimating would have to be much less uncertain than it is before there would be a dependable correlation between those operations making a loss and those where there was opportunity for cost reduction.

The principle of predictive control offers an alternative to conventional site cost control. If the object of such control is economy of site activity, it can only be realized if decisions involving selection of methods, allocation of resources, etc., lead to economy. It follows that control depends on predicting the cost of the alternatives available as accurately as possible, and then selecting the cheapest. Predictions made close to the event are less uncertain than those made some time ahead. Consequently, effective site cost control will result from thorough planning which is carried out in the fairly short term, and which uses recent cost records to make predictions of future costs.

Increasingly, contractors are having to take account of cash flow considerations, even in such short term control decisions. Economy may not be the only goal, it will be allied to making the best use of the capital locked-up in work. In earlier times when it was common for contracting companies to have cash reserves, profit on turnover was the only goal. Now, when the contracting division may be competing for allocation of capital with other divisions of a conglomerate group, the criterion of success is profit on the capital employed. Shareholders of contacting companies have always been principally interested in profit as a proportion of their capital employed. They are indifferent to the amount of turnover which has been necessary to produce the profit.

Decisions at a much lower level are having to be made with predictions of return on capital as an important criterion. Although in the textbook explanation of use of DCF rate of return it is usual to think of the choice between something like a thermal power station built now and a hydro-electric station built next year, in construction it is the rate of return that must be considered in deciding whether to hire in a certain piece of plant or to buy it, and whether to subcontract part of the work or not. Comparison of such alternatives on cost will produce decisions aimed at maximum profit on turnover. Comparison on the basis of rate of return from the expected cash flow will produce decisions aimed at maximum profit in proportion to capital used.

The growth of subcontracting in construction owes something to this factor: other things being equal, subcontracted work produces a higher rate of return for the main contractor than directly executed work. Taking this trend to its extreme produces the entrepreneur contractor carrying out no direct work. He achieves a miniscule profit on his turnover, but achieves an adequate return on capital. He must, however, exert a strong restraint on the amounts paid to his sub-contractors as his return on capital can easily disappear and the profit be lost by ineffective control.

Variations and extra work

Financial control requires that some function of the contractor's interest in the project is independent of any variations and extra work which is required. Usually, that function is considered to be his profit margin. This implies that he achieves the same percentage surplus of income over expenditure on varied work as on the work for which he originally contracted.

Other criteria are sometimes used for pricing variations. For example, the total amount of profit might be sustained instead of the percentage profit margin. This is equivalent to paying actual cost of varied work instead of paying prices commensurate with the contractor's original offer. A third criterion which has not to the author's knowledge been used yet would be to sustain the contractor's rate of return on capital. If this criterion were the contractor's internal maximizing objective, why should it not be used when adjusting payment to him?

At this stage in the project cycle, use of the 'unit cost/unit price' method shows further shortcomings. It must be accepted that the promoter pays for the site activity conducted by the contractor as well as for the materials used.

The plant, labour, and indirect costs contribute to the 'value' of the work done. Consequently, the valuation of variations to the work must particularly take account of these types of cost when they do not vary in direct proportion to the quantities of work completed. The value of work depends on how it was done as well as on what it looks like when it is finished. It is consequently wrong to value variations on the sole basis of unit prices for paticular completed components of the finished work.

Conventional adherence to this principle in contracts financially controlled by 'measure and value' is damaging to control. It produces changed valuation which is exaggerated in relation to the changes to the work. It makes the cost of any project to the promoter less predictable than it needs to be, and the profit achieved by the contractor less predictable than it needs be. The use of bills of quantities[1] embodying charges related to methods of working are aimed at this central problem of construction financial control. Originally devised for civil engineering contracts, the principles are now coming into use in the building industry.[3]

Post-contract settlement

In many types of construction project, the proportion of the payment for a contract which is decided unsystematically after the event is increasing. This is very damaging to control generally. Such 'horse deals' concluded at the end of construction can often influence the final cost to the client by 10%, and the profit or loss to the contractor by 200%.

The contractor's rate of return on investment is even more sensitive to the results of the deal. Since the later an unexpected or unpredictable payment comes in the project time cycle, the less foreknowledge of it can be used to exercise control, it is probably the most damaging feature of the systems of construction financial control used today.

Construction cost is part of the study of the feasibility of a project, is part of selection in design, and is the main criterion of predictive financial control generally. The amount of money which has to be predicted all through the cycle is the actual construction cost, the total amount finally paid to the contractor or contractors involved. Either cost is the main criterion, or it may be part of the assessment of present worth or rate of return. Because of claims negotiations, total cost is often not known until after completion.

It can probably be predicted closely just before the final negotiation, but prediction earlier in the project time-span is less accurate roughly in proportion to the length of time ahead of final settlement that the prediction or estimate is made. The distribution of probable error in the cost estimate is consequently widest at the feasibility study and narrows to zero only when the contractors have all been paid.

This is illustrated by Fig. 6.3. To explain the diagram consider the section line ABCD. Point A shows that the probability is one in three that the current cost estimate is 10% higher than the actual cost. Point B is the actual cost as yet unknown. Point C is the

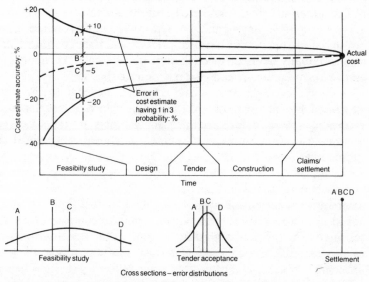

Probabilities and uncertainties in cost prediction are associated with particular stages in the project cycle. Cost prediction follows an evolution of continuously lessening uncertainty

Fig. 6.3. Chronology of cost estimate accuracy over the project time cycle

median of current estimates. Point D shows that the probability is one in three that the current estimate is 20% lower than the actual cost. The lower limit line is characteristically further separated from the actual than the upper limit line. No theoretical explanation can be offered for this, but if it were not so then contingency allowances would be negative as often as positive.

Data

It is important to consider the sources and reliability of data for financial control. Conventionally, cost control systems are said to be very vulnerable to poor data, both in terms of accuracy and timeliness. Estimating is thought to rely for data mainly on records from similar completed projects but, in reality, a lot of estimating is based on data assembled specifically for the current estimate. This applies not only to contractor's estimating but also to the estimating for feasibility studies and design decision making. There are two main reasons for this.

Firstly, few groups of estimators are working in sufficiently narrow and stable fields of engineering work that the proportion of data emerging from completed projects which is both relevant and up-to-date is very significant. Up-to-date in this context does not just mean current in terms of prices and currency values, but also current in terms of specifications of permanent components and of manufacturing and construction methods.

Secondly, few organizations have actually achieved the goal, often expressed by the cost control theorists, of having developed a recording system which enables actual costs to be allocated accurately or to a set of cost centres which are meaningful to estimators.

Fortunately, the more forward-looking approach to financial control generally which is advocated in this chapter relies less on assembly of accurate and up-to-date data than does the traditional approach. Experience shows that the benefit to control of concentrating on the remaining work instead of on the work completed to date is sufficient in itself to reduce the importance of data accuracy.

A simple example of this is provided by cost control during design. It is common in the engineering industries for design decisions to be taken on technical grounds without the cost implications of the design options being taken into account. A massive improvement in cost control will be achieved if the discipline of making cost forecasts for the options being considered in all significant design decisions is established. The benefit, increased probability of the completed design being capable of construction within the budget total, is sufficiently large that much of it will be achieved even if the data used is imprecise. It only has to be accurate enough to distinguish the options accurately. Only if the cost impacts of the options are similar does accuracy influence the answer. When the options are similar, the decision is likely, in any case, to be dominated by factors other than cost.

It often seems to be a shortcoming of engineers that they are uneasy using imprecise data. This uneasiness has to be overcome. In the financial control of engineering projects, precise data should be obtained and used as often as possible. But financial control is all to do with decisions and it is better to use imprecise cost data to help make decisions than to ignore cost implications.

Only the future of projects can be controlled. The only data about the future are forecasts. Forecasts can never be as accurate as records.

Conclusions

From the illustrations of application of predictive financial control already given, the main aims for improvement of techniques can be defined.

From the first idea in the mind of a promoter to the achievement of performance targets by the completed and operating installation, financial control demands that the cost and time effects of decisions are predicted. This requires that records of costs and times are kept in reproducible form, and that the amount paid for construction work is derived as systematically as possible. Controls must therefore be based on a realistic representation of the factors which influence the cost and timing of the work. Financial control can be measured by the accuracy with which the amounts and timing of all payments associated with the construction of the project can be predicted.

This concept of control is different from that advocated for service or manufacturing industry. Here control is exemplified by the Watt governor, quickly detecting divergence from the optimum pattern of activity and taking action to correct — stability is maintained. This is adequate for activities that remain unchanged over a control-

143

lable period. The concept is inapplicable to overall project control. Management of projects distinguishes itself from the management of other activities in that the objective is not to maintain stability. Instead, the object is to move from one state to another through a series of tasks, each of which can be very different from the one before and none of which may last for very long. Even apparently repetitive construction operations like tunnelling or multi-storey concrete frame construction change significantly as the distance from the portal or the ground increases. Effective project management often requires that change should be effected continuously and as quickly as possible.

Project control is the selection of a path through a network of alternatives. Each section is made according to which alternative is most likely to be a step towards the known objectives of technical performance, cost and completion date. The overriding criterion of effective financial control must be the ability to predict accurately the consequences on cost and time of the alternatives between which selection is made.

So that control decisions are not random it is necessary either to have records and experience of the outcome of comparable previous selections, or to be able to simulate the effect of the alternatives on the project in hand. Control is likely to be most effective if if actually draws on both.

Taking design decisions as an example, having used mathematics to simulate the stresses in a member, its design may be thought to be technically acceptable. Previous experience of bill of quantities prices can then be used to predict the likely cost of the member. If there is already a contract the cost of the member can be predicted using bill prices which will be used.

If the decision is not whether to include an extra member but whether to change the position of one already specified, the situation is more difficult. Bill of quantities prices will be no help as they do not represent the fact that perhaps a larger tower crane is necessary to place the member in its new position. If the contractor keeps records of cost in a pattern modelling cost factors closely, he will predict the cost closely, but the designer will be unable to do so from bill prices. This illustrates an important general principle. Construction financial control is hampered to the extent that the records and parameters of cost used to support decisions diverge from actual pattern of the separate factors which influence the costs of construction. This applies equally to decisions taken by the contractor, designer or any other controlling authority.

As explained in chapter 3, network analysis was rapidly adopted because it realistically represented the factors influencing the timing of construction and could be used to simulate the effect of selection between alternatives. It could offer answers to questions of the type 'when shall we finish if we do this instead of that?' A network can simulate dynamically where a bar chart can only represent one plan.

Simulation techniques (such as 'project cost model') can answer questions involving dynamic representation of the cost influencing factors in a project in the same way as network analysis is used to represent the time influencing factors. The application of the technique to financial control by the promoter is given in chapter 4.

Uncertainty from outside influences may be inevitable, but uncertainty within the service provided by the industry can be reduced by the use of a homogeneous group of control techniques and practices. Method-related bills of quantities and operational estimating, supported by cost models and networks, are such a group. These techniques are based on common principles which those responsible for control can recognize easily and use confidently.

Notes

1. Barnes, M. *The CESMM2 handbook*, Thomas Telford, London, 1986. See particularly the introduction and section 7 for commentary on method-related charges.
2. British Property Federation. *Manual of the BPF system*. BPF, London, 1983. An innovative approach to comprehensive and integrated control of project cost, time and performance. See particularly the use of activity schedules.
3. Royal Institute of Chartered Surveyors and Building Employers Confederation. *Standard method of measurement of building works* (SMM7), 7th edn. RICS and BEC, London, 1988.

7 Organization for control

In this short final chapter we consider the choices possible in industry in organizing responsibilities for the planning, monitoring and management of engineering projects, beginning with the simple systems that are sufficient for small or familiar investments and then going on to the ideas of matrix organizations and team responsibility that have more recently been evolved to integrate decisions for complex, novel and urgent projects.

In chapter 1 it was suggested that ideally everyone should be responsible for their own commitments. Where this is possible in industry and people can be largely self-sufficient in their work, they do not need to use the detailed methods of planning and monitoring described in this book. To satisfy financial pressures, whether in business or public service, they would need to control their costs, cash flow, speed and quality of work, but the more detailed methods of control available should be used only as needed to suit the objectives and complexity of a project or set of projects.

To limit the need to impose systems of control the principle should be to put people together in groups that can be self-sufficient and small enough for each member to understand what the others do.[1] This is an ideal aimed at in a current move in factories to reverse the division of manufacturing into repetitive and insignificant tasks.[2]

The bureaucratic trend in most industries has been to employ people as if they were machines, interchangeable within a specialization but not left free to adjust to individual abilities or approach the ideal of self-control. Financially, the economies of scale possible in repetitive production and in concentrating the use of services have been the attraction. They still are, especially in the poorer countries. Rates of growth have recently slowed down in many of the highly industrial countries, but projects generally continue to be technically and organizationally more complex, engineering decisions increasingly dependent on specialist knowledge, and working relationships ever more indirect and often only temporary for a particular project. Industry in most parts of the world is thus divided into sectors based on different technologies; public administration is similarly divided into many services, and within these people are employed in specialist departments and functions with only irregular contact or movement from one to another and only indirect links with their suppliers or with the eventual users of the goods or services produced.

Attention to the primary task

Engineers, accountants, and other specialists on entering industry are usually employed first on technical tasks with little or no dependence on people in other organizations or other departments. Detailed internal relationships thus provide the experience gained initially. When some progress to responsibility for managerial decisions on the design of an organization, they need a more strategic view — to turn from coping with internal tactics to anticipating changes in the expectations of customers, society and all involved. This transition is not always realized. Success in solving current problems does not guarantee the ability to think ahead. Experience of detail may not train people to perceive principles.

The relationships between people in organizations that they need to understand are usually complex and compounded of personal interests, habits, the demands of the work, the variety of individuals involved, their assumptions about each other, and the history of an organization and of its industry. In seeking to understand or to design an organization, it is therefore helpful to start by defining its *primary task*, the task or set of tasks essential to producing the goods or services to enable it to survive.[3] The primary task can then be analysed in order to determine the flow of information and decisions required to carry out its present and impending projects.

Organizational flow charts

A flow chart can show the logical relationships required.[4] The flow of information essential to the primary task can be drawn as a network, using the precedence diagram method described in

147

chapter 3, and each node then labelled to show the individual responsible for a decision and for issuing the results.

There is a risk for managers that producing such a chart can precipitate arguments or annoyance where it indicates that some members of an organization are greatly dependent on information from others. Such problems should be exposed by analysis rather than left hidden and cause recurrent conflicts. The practical attraction of using a flow chart to describe an organization is that it demonstrates everyone's contribution to the resulting product.

Choice of system

Given an analysis of working relationships required between them, people can be organized into groups to the extent justified by their numbers and the projects that provide their employment. Obviously, a system that is likely to arouse conflict or distort the primary task should be avoided. For instance, an excessive division of work that physically or psychologically keeps apart those most dependent on each other is no help. The location of departments in a firm and the layout of groups in offices influence greatly the pattern of communications in an organization. Divisions of work and physical separation have value where they assist in achieving safety from materials or security of information. Applying the principle stated earlier, a system should normally be designed to put together those who depend on each other for information, decisions, material or other resources. The less predictable the problems in the work, the less it should be split into planned tasks.

Most often in engineering organizations a variety of specialists need to divide their time and other resources amongst several projects. A choice or compromise is then needed between the simple alternatives of grouping together all those who are working on the same project or all those who are using common resources or applying a specialist expertise. These alternatives are known as the 'task force' system and the 'functional' system.

The systems of organization used vary greatly, depending on the relative importance given to peoples' interests and developing their 'know-how' compared with the shorter-term objectives of each project. Different arrangements can also be appropriate to each project in hand in one organization, and be varied from stage to stage in the work for them.

Real or assumed financial restraints usually limit the number

148

of people available, so that there is competition for them between projects and a risk of conflicts with individual and organizational objectives. A system does not automatically overcome this. Its use is in helping all concerned to perceive problems and try to achieve a collective result.

Hierarchies of management

Organizations in industry customarily employ group leaders, supervisors, foremen and others in similar roles who are expected to direct and control their groups' work under a 'hierarchy' of managers branching down from 'the top', this top level being the directors of a company, the chief officers in local government, the partners in a professional firm, etc. The division of responsibilities at each level is a means of establishing a system for making decisions on the employment of people and on the expenditure of resources allocated to them.

The hierarchical way of working is widely understood, but in practice it is too simple to be completely satisfactory. Partly, this is due to social changes not particular to industry — that the language and concept of being 'under' others in a 'chain-of-command' are less and less acceptable to many people. The traditional, though perhaps always uncertain, paternal duty of leaders to look after 'their' people is no longer sufficient. Much more influential today are the financial pressures on managers exerted from above and from outside their organization. Consumers, governments, managers and all of us expect value for money, but in industrial nations there is an increasing remoteness from the effects of financial decisions on the employment of other people. It is this remoteness of decision-making that is questionable. Study of these general social trends is beyond the scope of this book, but their effects on the choice of feasible control systems in industry must be considered. Assuming that reform is preferable to revolution, it may be satisfied by increasingly consultative planning before decisions are made and by the sophistication of the principle of hierarchical responsibilities to try to retain its advantages while adapting it to meet these more complex demands.

Operationally also, the hierarchical basis for managerial relationships is inadequate to cope with the recycling of decisions that is increasingly required in carrying out projects to adjust to changes from the initial predictions of their value and their cost. Though many projects are expected to be completed as planned, the information initially available for predicting the external demand, the costs of finance, the effects of decisions by other organizations and changes in public policy on safety, pollution, employment, etc., can alter significantly before a sanctioned proposal is completed. At the same time, the progress of some sections of the work is likely to vary and changes may be needed to overcome technical, contractual or manpower problems or the coincidence of several such uncertainties, in addition to the novel features inherent in a proposal that should have been perceived and studied before its sanctioning.

All these uncertainties vary from project to project, but they are generally becoming more significant in every industry. Estimates of value and of cost therefore have to be thought of as probabilistic, as discussed in chapter 6, and decisions based on these estimates should be increasingly considered as provisional and subject to revisions stage by stage in proceeding with sanctioned projects.

Traditionally, in a hierarchy the authority to make decisions has stemmed from the top, and been successively subdivided at each level downwards through the system. Recommendations should go up. Decisions should come down. Those are the classical ideas. Certainly any such system is formed from the top, given the authority to incur the expenditure of resources to employ people. Rarely is an organization in industry formed co-operatively by the people who carry out the primary task. Horizontal or 'lateral' collaboration is therefore neither the customary start to relationships between the people employed nor is it given credit under the vertical financial pressures. Competition is more the mode. Yet the increasing uncertainties of predicting demands or public policy and of predicting the costs and success of the engineering have made it more and more vital to develop collaborative decision-making in organizations so as to be able to adjust to external changes or internal problems at any stage in the work for a project.[5]

Managerial capacity

The hierarchical system of authority has the advantage that one or a few people at the top are clearly responsible for the whole organization, particularly for authorizing the use of resources and accounting for the results. If they can foresee problems, they can define who should resolve them. In theory, the authority to make decisions should be delegated down to the lowest level concerned, so that the higher levels are free to look ahead, deal with the exceptional unforeseen problems, and plan innovations and the development of people and the system so as to be able to continue to survive.

This theory corresponds to much of what happens but, as has already been stated, the use of authority depends on more and more attention to human relationships, social consequences, and unforeseen problems. Continuing managerial attention to each project once sanctioned is required, so as to react and control reactions to unpredicted changes. As is common experience in industry, less and less can therefore be delegated in the hierarchical way and managers are eventually overwhelmed. First lost is their time to look ahead, so compounding the problems.

Individuals' capacity to cope can be developed by training in analysing problems and in applying techniques together with studies to compare alternative ideas and experience. Time off the job for this purpose can also help them to shed interests or habits irrelevant to their objectives, but does not finally answer the increasing demand for continuing attention to decisions. Organizational means are also required.

Numbers

The most obvious but in practice the least valuable way of giving managers more time is to add more of them to share the work. The number of levels in a managerial system and the number of managers at each level are logically a function of the complexity and unpredictability of their project decisions, the extent that these are dependent on outside or uncontrollable factors, and how much the managers involved have experience of making these decisions and of working with each other. Little or nothing is gained by adding to a hierarchy vertically or horizontally, as all those in the system then have to use more time in co-ordination between themselves.[6]

Staff roles

Widely used in practice is the 'line-and-staff' principle of assistants to managers. The managers in the *line* of the hierarchy remain responsible for the decisions and results, a *staff* role in prin-

151

ciple being an extention to a line role and not an addition to the numbers in the hierarchy. Staff may be individually appointed to assist one manager or be grouped in a department to provide a service to all. Formally, such systems do not alter the authority or the responsibilities of the line managers, but can add to their capacity for studying information, assessing trends, preparing papers and investigating results.

The staff role may be designed to be educational for the line managers, by providing them with assistants who have different experience, more theoretical training, or simply the time to study innovations elsewhere. In return it can offer a wide view of problems to the inexperienced assistant.

Although not relevant to the present subject of project control, employment in staff departments provides the major means of offering careers to specialists separately from the managerial progression up a hierarchy, in supporting functions such as research, computing, contracts, personnel services, and work study.

The line-and-staff principle can be used in several ways to assist in the control of projects as follows.

Project evaluation and sanctioning

Observations in engineering have shown that useful project ideas can come from anywhere in or beyond an organization, and that relatively informal meetings between people with different knowledge and interests are often successful means of innovation and of solving novel problems.

The study of future needs and ideas can therefore be the function of a *staff* team in an organization, given either to a set of managers' assistants or to a mixed group of specialists bringing together their experience of recently completed projects. However arranged, they need to have the time to discuss alternatives and consider the interaction of several ideas.

Such groups incurring only a minor proportion of an organization's total costs are one way in which staff can augment line management. The latter have the authority on the use of the major resources employed on the primary task. In chapter 2 it was stated that the investments essential to the survival of an organization should be selected and authorized by the 'top' management. Their staff can have the function of improving the prior study of proposals.

Planning and budgeting

Specialists in planning methods and specialists in engineering costs are also usually employed as staff services, to provide expertise in techniques and to link proposals to use resources required for more than one project.

In chapter 3 the alternative possible systems of relationships between the managers of projects and the specialists in planning were listed, with the conclusion that the latter could best contribute a planning service with the expertise and time to study and monitor detail, but that the line managers must direct the policy for each project and exert the control actions.

The same is appropriate in employing specialists in estimating and cost monitoring. They apply different expertise to that of planners, utilizing more specific information particular to a project rather than general techniques evolved over a series of projects, but the services of these to a project need to be integrated with those of planning so that both the time and the money effects of decisions are considered in all recommendations. Though contributing different techniques and expertise developed in different time spans, planning and budgeting staff should work together to serve projects jointly.

Systems staff

Although the apparent or expedient sharing of authority between line and staff can cause uncertainties in organizations, the idea is widely practised to provide managers with supporting expertise in techniques and to augment their capacity to study alternative ideas, handle detail and investigate results. There remains the problem that organizations however well evolved become out-of-date. So can the specialists employed in staff roles. One remedy is to employ some staff to review the organization and the expertise it needs.

An organization can thus logically grow into a 'system of systems', the successful pattern of the analogous evolution of brains and methods of control.[7] As defined earlier, the primary level in industry should be based on the working relationships essential in the engineering. At the secondary level is the system of decision-making, supported by the tertiary system of staff. An internal learning and reviewing system is another, and to complete the logic a system for anticipating external trends is also needed. In this way a managerial organization can be designed with the task of sanctioning the use of resources and served with intelligence on external changes, evaluations of ideas, analyses of the organization and feedback from the progress of current projects. When a project is sanctioned the authority to use resources can be passed down through a hierarchy of responsibilities, at each level support being given in planning, estimating and monitoring the remaining work.

This is logical. It need not be complex. Thinking ahead, looking at changing demands, assessing new ideas, reviewing the organization and controlling the sanctioned projects do not have to be separate tasks. But they must be done. When one person has all these to do the danger is that the demands of immediate problems take up the time intended to be used for forward thinking. Hence the logic of setting staff aside for this purpose.

Project execution

Allowing for their adaptation to individuals, hierarchical and line-and-staff ideas are quite well understood in industrial and other organizations, and they are commonly used in organizing the study, evaluation, planning and sanctioning of projects.

In the subsequent stages of carrying out projects practice varies more, notably because the work then depends on greater numbers of people who differ more in their specializations and may be in geographically or commercially separate organizations. As mentioned at the start of this chapter, engineering and other resources are mostly organized in specialist firms, departments, etc., so as to be employed on a series of projects. Each therefore depends on transitory relationships that have to be established stage by stage in the work and usually in competition with other projects and the interests of each participant.

Probabilistic control

As discussed earlier, there is an increasing need in all industries to develop the capacity to recycle decisions in carrying out engineering projects, using improved predictions of demand, etc., together with reviews of progress, etc., to re-evaluate the investment and revise the plans, budgets and objectives for completing the remaining work. To reduce the volume of detail that would have to be recycled back through the top management who sanction projects, they can delegate authority to vary budgets, etc., with the responsibility for monitoring and adjusting plans within specified objectives. The cost-time-value equation of the objectives should be defined for this, so as to guide the remaining decisions in design and the revision of plans to overcome problems.

Knowledge of the statistical accuracies of estimating provides a rational basis for delegating this authority. A contingency sum can be decided that has for example a 4:1 chance of being adequate to meet uncertainties in the estimating and planning, and authority to exert control within this range of cost be delegated with the responsibility for monitoring.

Organization of control

The authority to make the decisions affecting the cost, time and value of projects can be arranged in the following alternative ways, the choice in any case logically depending on the urgency and complexity of a project and its importance to the investing organization.

Functional responsibility

The responsibility for a project can be delegated to one manager in the hierarchy of an organization, either because his department does most of the work involved in carrying it out, or because it is the eventual user of the completed investment. These alternatives tend to have different results: the eventual user or customer is likely to take a longer-term view in making decisions; for instance, in design, considering the reliability of plant and economic maintenance as relatively more important than innovations predicted to offer relatively small economies compared with established practice.

Giving authority to the 'customer' is logical where the resulting reliability and economy of a project is important, provided that a policy on innovation has been applied in the study stage before sanctioning. Giving the authority for control to the main contributor to a project is logical where decisions depend on expertise not possessed by the customer, provided that a policy on controlling changes is applied after the sanctioning.

Committees

Forming a committee of managers to resolve conflicts of interests is not popular in industry, probably because committees diffuse

155

accountability and can take up much of people's time. Where expertise and interests overlap, a steering committee formed of the managers whose departments contribute to a project is potentially valuable to provide a reserve means of resolving conflicts. But rather than try collectively to follow the volume of detail in carrying out a project, they can better delegate this to one person acting interdepartmentally who has the time to anticipate problems.

Project leaders

Individuals have been appointed to do this and labelled project manager, project engineer, product co-ordinator, etc. in engineering in recent years. Their significance varies from case to case, depending on the people involved as well as the systems of organization utilizing them, but the idea common to all these is that one person should monitor all the work directly or indirectly contributing to one project.

This can be a co-ordinating or progress chasing role, in which the individual controls only himself. It can be more, with some control over information, the budget, the planning and the formal communications linking all working on the project. The project leader can be the hierarchical manager of all employed on one project, a system appropriate for an investment of such importance, novelty, urgency or geographical remoteness that justifies not sharing resources or experience with others.

Experience and research indicates that one person should have the time, expertise and authority to be in control. The tendency in some industries has been to add project roles reluctantly, perhaps responsible to a steering committee. More than this may be needed, particularly sufficient authority to be able to avoid or at least control problems as they arise. Every project needs a project director with this authority either separately or as part of other responsibilities. A typical job specification for this role is given in Appendix 1.[8]

Matrix relationship

The word *matrix* is used to describe a system that includes project leaders to link related decisions across the vertical lines of a hierarchy of established departmental managers, group leaders, etc. This word has probably come to be a name for such arrangements because the combination of vertical and horizontal relationships resembles a mathematical matrix.

It accurately describes systems in which the project leaders are expected to co-ordinate decisions that are made by the line management and the latter remain responsible for people, material resources and decisions. In practice, as a project proceeds these co-ordinators become the most knowledgeable on how choices in overcoming problems can best meet the project objectives; increasingly if there is confidence in them as individuals they may make the decisions jointly with the specialists working on the detail.

Compound management

There have thus evolved systems in which decisions are the responsibility of both the line and the project managers. These are also commonly known as 'matrix' systems, although they are more complex than implied by that word: mathematically speaking, they amount to a sharing of authority.

Compound systems of this type were first used in organizations carrying out large and technically complex projects. The idea of joint decision making has general value, applicable to any work down to the one man task. It is a means of recognizing formally that solving problems depends on combining specialist expertise in the detail consequent on a choice of solution and the drive and knowledge to get decisions made that best meet project objectives.

Anticipation of problems is the task of all managers. In compound systems the project leaders need to be involved in sufficient detail to anticipate problems in completing their projects, whereas the general and specialist managers in the hierarchy need to be involved in sufficient studies of external and other changes to anticipate problems extending beyond the projects already sanctioned.

The sophistication of responsibilities and relationships required takes time to become effective in organizations to which it is added. A maturing process is needed for recognizing the value of this systematic means of attending to the increasingly recyclic patterns of decisions in investing in a new product, process, structure or any such project.

Project teams

The study of proposals for projects can be the task of a team drawn from most or all the specializations involved in carrying out projects, to draw together their experience and ideas from the start.

The team can continue until completion of their project, to prepare decisions on the problems that arise due to external changes or internally in the work of proceeding with the investment. Whether meeting only occasionally to discuss actions on a small project or working together full-time until completion of a complex one, such a team is a valuable means of unifying objectives and of achieving a continuity of knowledge of the reasons for decisions. To do both, a team should include members drawn from all stages of work for the project, particularly from the people who have to accept the results of decisions. For its members there is also a longer-term training value to be obtained from jointly studying problems and experiencing the consequences of decisions through to the end of a project.

Within a managerial system a team may have only a co-ordinating function, like an individual project leader with a linking role in a matrix. Or the team leader can be authorized to make decisions that commit all departments, because of the complexity, novelty, urgency or special importance of the project. In any case the members of a team tend to make the decisions on detail. Their collective authority should be defined stage by stage, not least to avoid confusion — for instance where sections of a project may get to what is considered 'detail' before others.

Although a team representing all interests can work together and approach the ideal group that shares tasks and achieves control, a leader or chairman is usually appointed to be accountable for the team and their links with the rest of the organization or other organizations. In some examples a project leader is selected from the team which prepared the proposal for sanctioning. The leadership can change later to another member more experienced in the remaining work or in the subsequent use of the completed project.

Meetings

Meetings are characteristic of work in many organizations. They can be useful but need to be planned. A check-list for planning them is given in Appendix 2.[9]

Contracts

Employing contractors to undertake part or all of the work for a project can free the investing 'promoter' of some risks and the detail of control, but in a way that is analogous to delegating the

158

authority for carrying out a project to a department within the promoter's organization. Whether going to contract or not, the greater the probabilities that decisions will have to be recycled, the greater the need for the investor to plan ahead to define the responsibility for anticipating problems and the authority to revise commitments.

The choices for promoters in deciding their systems of organization for the control of contracts are therefore similar in principle to those already mentioned in this chapter. One established manager can be designated as the employer of a contractor, and his department supervise the work — to the extent that the promoter is concerned with the detail of the progress and quality of the contractor's work.[10] Or a separate project leader can be appointed, or a team formed. To support any of these alternatives a separate organization such as consulting engineers can also be employed to provide services stage by stage and to supervise a contractor.

Whereas a promoter is usually concerned with the capital cost and the longer-term value of his investment and the calculations considered in chapters 2 and 4, a contractor has a shorter-term concern to achieve the most economic use of resources on the projects in hand, the calculations considered in chapters 5 and 6. Contractors' systems of management designed to control the detail of projects under way or about to start therefore logically differ from those of the promoters employing them. Differences in form, authority and size are particularly obvious in the site organizations of promoters and of contractors for controlling the construction and commissioning of a capital project. Project management generally tends to be more authoritative and a line role in contracting organizations, except that relatively weak arrangements of project co-ordinators remain common practice where the contractor is both the manufacturer and the erector of capital plant or where a group of contractors are acting together as a temporary consortium.

Conclusions

One conclusion of observing practice in the various branches of engineering is that there is no one right system of organization nor a universal technique of control that all should use. There are choices. These should be considered deliberately and starting from the needs of the projects that make up the primary task in each case. Theory and practice show that people should be grouped together in a logical way, designed according to the importance of project objectives relative to the longer-term value of developing expertise. External and internal variables have to be analysed, to be able to anticipate changing needs and to learn from the consequences of the use of a system and supporting techniques.

Another general conclusion is that within many organizations the system for controlling a project differs from one stage of the work to the next. Engineering organizations in all sectors of industry are commonly based on a hierarchical system of authority for sanctioning the use of resources on a project, but they have increasingly evolved consultative relationships to draw together ideas, experience and interests for the prior stage of preparing proposals; and subsequently they also increasingly use collaborative systems of project management in order to control the responses of all involved to problems and changes in the predictions of external or internal variables affecting the value and cost of a sanctioned project.

Talk of 'project management' and its techniques has become quite common. Is it too much emphasized today? Is it only a passing fashion? May be, to some extent. Some enthusiasm and a process of trials and error are usual in achieving improvements. For instance, the experience gained in many industries that some applications of network techniques of planning have been expected to achieve too much can be learnt by others, particularly when the uncertainties inherent in the information fed in have been forgotten when using the results. Techniques cannot control the uncontrollable, in evaluating, planning, estimating or monitoring a project. But such techniques do have continuing value in making people look ahead and see which uncertainties may be most critical to completing a project. Attention to project management in general has been justifiable because of the growing complexity and cost of projects, not least for the many engineers whose training when students did not include the study of some theory and examples of economics, organization and project control that are available in courses today. Expertise in project management and the systems to make use of it seem to be maturing in many sections of industry, through experience and supported by courses and collaborative research and development such as that on cost control referred to in chapters 4 and 6.

There is no obvious reason why engineering will not have to be increasingly adaptable and continue to evolve its systems and techniques to meet changes in public policy, markets, decisions by other organizations and any variables that are largely or entirely beyond the control of industry. Society is increasingly dependent on engineering for services essential to its supplies of food, water, housing and most material things, but in return for its employment, engineering is increasingly likely to have to respond to demands and be prepared to present flexible proposals for discussion of alternative effects on people, the use of land and the consumption of other resources. Projects seem likely to be more and more subject to public criteria. The resources required to carry out essential and agreed projects are likely to become increasingly costly and some quite rare. All the more important for engineers, accountants and all involved to be able to control projects once sanctioned.

Notes

1. A number of assertions and simplifications appear here and elsewhere in this chapter. Readers should preferably go on to study the textbooks referred to, but with the caution that not all that is in print is supported by evidence.
2. Handy, C. *Understanding organizations*, 3rd edn. Penguin, London, 1985.
3. For a classical study of designing organizations to meet their social and technical needs see Miller, E.J. and Rice, A.K. *Systems of organization.* Tavistock, 1967.
4. The case study of John Hall Boilers Ltd, which can be purchased from the Cranfield School of Management, illustrates how the flow of information can be used to analyse and design an organization.
5. Although attention to systems of organization is increasingly needed in business and public services, not least to make the most of managers' abilities to cope with the ever greater uncertainties and complexity of decisions, it does not follow that more formal relationships are appropriate. Study of existing practice in organizations shows that some systems should not only be altered but also that they should be relaxed to become more organic.
6. Assessing the efficiency of a managerial system can therefore start with recording how time is used and comparing the results with individuals' forecasts of the needs of their work. A reduction in numbers can be one result.

7. For a detailed essay on cerebral analogies with managerial systems see Beer, S. *The brain of the firm.* Allen Lane, 1972.
8. Ninos, G.E. and Wearne, S.H. *Responsibilities for project control during construction.* University of Bradford, 1984, report TMR 17.
9. Scott, W.P. Control of meetings. *Proc. Instn Civ. Engrs*, Part 1, 1983, **74**, 909—916.
10. Promoters' checking of contractors' planning and work in detail, because of their longer-term concern for quality, safety and costs of time, can be expensive. It is also possible that this double checking unintentionally reduces the effectiveness of contractors' management. Defining principles for checking contractors' planning and other work is therefore needed in project management.

Appendix 1 Job specification for a project director

The following job specification has been drafted for use in large organizations. More simple versions may often be adequate, depending on the complexity of a project, its urgency and the contractual responsibilities of promoter, consultants and contractors. This job specification is therefore intended to be used as a check-list. The detail in it should be selected according to what is appropriate to a project and who is responsible for its planning, costing and control.

Job title: Project Director
Responsible to: Project Board
Supervising: Project Team

Overall job objective
  To direct the design, construction and taking over of the project to achieve its objectives within the total cost and completion time authorized by the Project Board.

Authority
  The Project Director has the responsibility and the authority to make or delegate all decisions needed to achieve the project objectives within the target cost and completion time authorized by the Project Board.
  The Project Director has no authority to vary the objectives, target cost or completion date except in emergencies.

Job responsibilities
- To keep the project objectives, costs and progress under review and make recommendations to the Project Board for changes to the project brief, budgets or programme.
- To advise the Project Board of the financial, managerial and other resources required for the project.

163

- To advise the Project Board of all decisions and actions required of the Board or the Project Promoter, preferably giving dates related to the programme for design, construction and taking over.
- To appoint the Project Team Leader (unless the project is small enough for the Project Director to be the Team Leader), define the authority and responsibility in writing to the person and all interested parties, supervise the Project Team Leader, and keep the appointment under review.
- To appoint the Project Team, define their authority and responsibilities in writing to the Team and all interested parties, and keep these appointments under review.
- To motivate the Project Team.
- To develop the knowledge and skills of the Project Team.
- To instruct the Project Team on the project brief.
- To appoint the Engineer or equivalent for contracts, if in the opinion of the Project Director such appointments are needed, define the authority and responsibility of each appointment in writing to each and all interested parties, and keep each under review.
- To keep the system of control of design and construction under review and make changes that appear to be needed to achieve the project objectives.
- To instruct the Project Team on the policy and procedures for the employment of consultants and contractors.
- To appoint consultants and contractors.
- To issue changes to the project brief etc. to the Project Team, if authorized by the Project Board or if in the opinion of the Project Director an emergency requires a change before the Project Board can be consulted.
- To report to the Project Board on the progress, cost, quality and predicted results of design and construction, at regular intervals specified by the Board and as soon as practicable after emergency changes.
- To instruct the Project Team on instituting and maintaining a project information system, particularly on project design, specifications and tests, budget, costs, programmes, progress, predictions and decisions on problems, decisions on changes and reasons for decisions.
- To plan the run-down of the Project Team.
- To consult the Project Team.

Qualifications needed
- Successful performance as team leader and site manager of

projects comparable in their technical nature and managerial uncertainties.

- Ability to make decisions despite uncertainty in relationships and information.
- Training in risk analysis.
- Motivation to make the project a success.
- Self-control in the use of time.
- Ability to communicate and motivate.
- Knowledge of the promoter's organization and ways of making decisions.

Appendix 2 Use of meetings

Meetings are common at all stages of all but the simplest projects. Their uses and efficiency vary greatly. Well-run meetings can be valuable for agreeing facts, committing people to objectives, locating problems, generating answers to problems and achieving a team spirit. Meetings which are vague in purpose or lacking relevant people can waste time and demoralize a project. Meetings should therefore be planned. The following is a check-list for that purpose.

Possible objectives of meetings
- To introduce parties together, not least members of different departments in the promoter's organization.
- To describe a project, its objectives and its programme.
- To obtain ideas and views on problems and potential problems.
- To provide and check information.
- To make decisions.
- To issue instructions.
- To receive reports.

Check-list for planning meetings
- Decide purpose
o select one or more of the above

- Decide attendance
o one meeting attended by all parties?
o separate internal and contract meetings?
o separate meetings with each party?
o separate meetings at operational, specialist and managerial levels?

- Decide time
o as problems arise?
o regular time and date?
o at key dates or changes in responsibility?
o at call of any party?

- Decide procedure
  - formal prior agenda?
  - minutes to state decisions only, or decisions and reasons?
  - minutes to be contractual?
  - minutes to be written during or after meeting?
  - minutes to be formally ratified?
  - minutes to go to?

- Decide control
  - authority of chairman
  - commitment of managers?

Bibliography

Andersen, E.S. *et al. Goal-directed project management.* Kogan Page, London, London, 1987.

British Institute of Management, *Total project management* BIM, London, series of booklets.

Cleland, D.I. and King, W.R. *Systems analysis and project management,* 3rd edn. McGraw-Hill, 1983.

Hajek, V.G. *The management of engineering projects,* 3rd edn. McGraw-Hill, 1984.

Harrison, F.L. *Advanced project management* 2nd edn. Gower, Aldershot, 1985.

Institution of Civil Engineers. *Crucial problems in the management of projects overseas.* ICE, London, 1988.

Lock, D. *Project Management,* 3rd edn. Gower, Aldershot, 1984.

Morris, P.W.G. and Hough, G.H. *The anatomy of large projects.* Wiley, 1987.

National Economic Development Office. *Guidelines for the management of major projects in the process industries,* London NEDO, 1982.

Stallworthy, E.A. and Kharbanda, O.P. *A guide to project implementation.* Institution of Chemical Engineers, London, 1986.

Taylor, W.J. and Watling, T.F. *Successful project management,* 2nd edn. Business Books and Bookfield Publishing, 1979.

Biographies

M. W. Allen, *MBA, CEng, MIMechE, MIProdE, MBIM, ACMA*
Mike Allen served a seven-year technical apprenticeship at Vauxhall
Motors in the USA. After returning to the UK he worked in the
Vauxhall Motors supplier quality assurance department as a senior
QA engineer responsible for the quality of bought-out chassis
components.

After studying for his MBA at Cranfield School of Management
in 1976–77 he was appointed a lecturer in finance and accounting at Cranfield. In addition to lecturing he was involved in
research, writing for publications, management accounting activities
at Cranfield, and he also spent a short period working at ICI Plastics
Division. In January 1980 he joined Babcock Power as a project
accountant and later qualified for membership of the Chartered
Institute of Management Accountants. Afterwards he worked as
project accountant at Kent Process Control, and principal management accountant at the Guided Weapons Division of British
Aerospace.

Mr Allen returned to Cranfield in October 1983. In addition to
lecturing on the MBA, MSc, and various short-course programmes,
he has also taught on finance courses in the USA and Mexico. He
has also co-authored a book with Professor D.R. Myddelton on
essential management accounting which was published by
Prentice-Hall.

N. M. L. Barnes, *BSc(Eng), PhD, FEng, FICE, FCIOB,
ACIArb, MBCS*
Martin Barnes is a partner in Martin Barnes Project Management,
which is part of the international accounting and business services
organization of Deloitte Haskins & Sells.

He is the chairman of the Association of Project Managers and a member of the Legal Affairs and Standard Method of Measurement committees of the Institution of Civil Engineers.

Dr Barnes has been a specialist in engineering and construction project management since 1968. His firm manages construction projects on a broad front for clients in the UK and assists with management on projects worldwide. Dr Barnes has advised on the management of projects such as Eurotunnel, the Greater Cairo wastewater scheme for the government of Egypt, and the Eastern Scheldt Barrier for the government of the Netherlands. He is an adviser to the World Bank on dealing with inflation and multiple currencies on international projects.

He is an expert on contracts and cost control, and was responsible for preparing the sixth and seventh editions of the building standard method of measurement and of the first and second editions of the civil engineering standard method of measurement. He has been appointed by the Institution of Civil Engineers to design a new style contract which will embody improved techniques of management and control for the benefit of employers, contractors and subcontractors.

D. B. L. Elliott, *BSc*

David Elliott graduated in physics in 1948. After several years in the Instructor Branch of the Royal Navy he went into development in the instrument industry. He then worked in the chemical industry for eight years, initially on developing automation systems and later on planning and plant improvement studies. He followed this with a period in the food industry running a management services department. More recently he has been in charge of data processing training for one of the main clearing banks.

T. J. Evans, *BSc, CEng, FIMechE, FIMinE, MBIM*

After graduating, John Evans taught mechanical engineering at the Hatfield Polytechnic for six years. Following this academic phase he joined the Shell Group. He worked initially at Shellhaven refinery, followed by a period in the Hague, where he was responsible for the co-ordination of the procurement of major chemical and oil plant projects on an international basis.

After seven years with Shell he entered the contracting industry, joining Babcock & Wilcox in South Africa as chief project manager.

170

He had responsibility for the project management and project engineering of various energy-related projects in southern Africa. In 1980 he rejoined Babcock in the UK, and held various senior positions in their contracting group.

Mr Evans joined the Taylor Woodrow Group in 1987 and is currently managing director of one of their mechanical engineering contracting companies Birtley Engineering Ltd.

K. J. Kelsey, *FCIS, Barrister*

Kenneth Kelsey was born in 1923. He has spent the major part of his career with the Babcock & Wilcox group engaged on the financial and cost control of engineering. Between 1951 and 1965 he was variously assistant secretary, chief accountant and company secretary of Dewrance & Co. Ltd where he was responsible for the cost and financial control of that company and its subsidiaries. Between 1965 and 1968 he was secretary/accountant to the Boiler and Nuclear Engineering Division of Babcock & Wilcox Ltd, responsible for the financial control and profit evaluation of Babcock's major contracts. He was the company's representative on the Water Tube Boilermakers Association's working party which negotiated revised increased cost formulae, terms of contract and planned payments with the CEGB. In 1968 he was apppointed secretary/accountant of Babcock UK Investments Ltd, the Babcock offshoot responsible for broadening the company's base by diversifying mainly into the contractor's plant and equipment industry.

Mr Kelsey left Babcock in 1970 to become the financial director of the Watney Mann subsidiary engaged on a programme of hotel and leisure development throughout Europe. On that company's acquisition he became a director of Galliford Estates Ltd, responsible for their major programme of developments overseas. He formed his own project management and consultancy company in 1976, but is now retired.

R. A. Milligan, *BSc(Eng), CEng, MIMechE*

Ronald Milligan, a graduate in mechanical engineering of London University, joined the former Salt Division of ICI in 1950 for postgraduate training and subsequent appointments in plant management, operations research, project design and commissioning. After transferring to the Dyestuffs (later 'Organics') Division of ICI in 1960 he spent a period of design engineering work on nylon projects. He was subsequently appointed as works maintenance engineer and, in 1965, division planning engineer when he concentrated his attention on the development of simplified planning and project control techniques. This period was followed by his appointment to senior project engineer for two successive dyestuffs intermediates projects and later for polyurethanes projects.

In 1980 Mr Milligan joined British Nuclear Fuels plc at Risley initially to become a member of a newly formed Project Management Group. Up to his retirement in 1986 he was involved in the management of projects for new waste handling and treatment plants at Sellafield. He is currently a member of a British Standards Institution committee concerned with project management methods and techniques.

P. A. Thompson, *BSc(Eng), MSc, CEng, FICE, MIWES*
Peter Thompson is the AMEC Professor of Engineering Project Management at the University of Manchester Institute of Science and Technology. After graduating at Queen Mary College, he completed his professional training with Sir William Halcrow & Partners, consulting engineers. He then worked with an oil company and later spent three years on site during the construction of Hinkley Point A nuclear power station. Subsequently he joined Binnie & Partners, consulting engineers, and became project manager on major water supply projects.

Since moving to UMIST Professor Thompson has specialized in the contractual and managerial aspects of project management and has initiated and supervised numerous research and development projects in collaboration with industry. These include the CIRIA studies on bills of quantities, target cost and management contracts. He has been responsible for the preparation of cost estimates and contract documents for projects in Africa, the Middle East, the Far East and Europe, and is regularly involved in project management training in many parts of the world. Current assignments include a contract strategy report in the Middle East, a study of estimating techniques and procedures for the ODA, and research into risk assessment and management.

S. H. Wearne, *BSc(Eng), DIC, PhD, CEng*
Stephen Wearne is a consultant, and works with the Project Management Group at the University of Manchester Institute of

Science and Technology on problems of projects and contract management. He also leads short courses run by the engineering institutions and in-company training.

He was originally a mechanical apprentice and sandwich course student. After training in water power engineering he worked on the design, economic planning and co-ordination of projects in Spain, Scotland and South America. In 1957 he joined turnkey contractors on construction and design and then contract and project management of projects in the UK and Japan. In 1964 he moved into research and teaching on engineering management, first at the University of Manchester Institute of Science and Technology, and from 1973 to 1984 as Professor of Technological Management at the University of Bradford. His research has included studies of design and project organizations, engineering and construction contracts, project control, plant commissioning teams, and the managerial tasks of engineers in their careers. He was the first chairman of the UK Engineering Project Management Forum initiated in 1985 by the National Economic Development Office and the Institutions of Civil, Mechanical, Electrical and Chemical Engineers.